Midwives in Passage

Social and Economic Studies No. 44
Institute of Social and Economic Research
Memorial University of Newfoundland

Midwives in Passage

The Modernisation of Maternity Care

Cecilia M. Benoit

ISER

**Institute of Social and
Economic Research**

© Institute of Social and Economic Research 1991
Memorial University of Newfoundland
St. John's, Newfoundland
Canada
ISBN 0-919666-70-1

Printed on paper
containing over 50%
recycled paper including
5% post-consumer fibre.   ∞   Printed in Canada on acid-free paper

Canadian Cataloguing in Publication Data

Benoit, Cecilia, 1954-

Midwives in passage

(Social and economic studies, ISSN 0847-0898 ;
no. 44)

Includes bibliographical references and index.
ISBN 0-919666-70-1

1. Midwives -- Cross-cultural studies.
2. Midwives -- Newfoundland. 3. Maternal health
services -- Government policy. I. Memorial
University of Newfoundland. Institute of Social and
Economic Research. II. Title. III. Series: Social
and economic studies (St. John's, Nfld.) ; no. 44.

RG950.B56 1991   362.1'9820233   C91-097618-X

For Oswald Hall, a singular teacher

The effective freedom to choose one's special line of work, to have access to the appropriate clients and equipment, to engage in that converse with eager and competent colleagues which will sharpen one's knowledge and skill, to organise one's time and effort so as to gain that end, and even freedom from pressure to conform to clients' individual or collective customs and opinions seem, in many lines of work, to be much greater for those professionals who have employers ...than for those who, according to the traditional concept, are in independent practice.

Everett Hughes 1966:69–70

Contents

Acknowledgements

In preparing this study, I have greatly benefitted from the support of family, friends, colleagues, and teachers. Conversations with my late mother, Rita, first awakened my interest in the midwifery occupation. Lesley Biggs set me on the right course by helping me to differentiate between the sociology and the politics of midwifery. I am also grateful to the Toronto midwives and their clients whom I interviewed, and to Kay Matthews and numerous Newfoundland and Labrador midwives who, with great frankness, discussed topics which intimately touch upon their lives and careers.

I wish to thank Robert Brym, Doug House, Nancy Mandell, Jane Lewis, Jean Briggs, Sheryl Ruzek, and two anonymous reviewers for the Social Science Federation of Canada for helpful comments on various parts of the manuscript. I am also grateful for the support of Robert Paine, Kevin Pittman, and the secretarial staff at Memorial University of Newfoundland's Institute of Social and Economic Research. Judith Adler offered intellectual stimulation and emotional support during the entire study. Her concern and her insights have been invaluable. I owe special thanks to Volker Meja, but cannot even begin to state my indebtedness to him here, and to Oswald Hall, without whose patience, humour, and probing for complexity this book might not have been possible.

This book has been published with the help of a grant from the Social Science Federation of Canada, using funds provided by the Social Sciences and Humanities Research Council of Canada.

Map: Labrador

Cartography: Memorial University Cartographic Laboratory. Courtesy of Office of
the Queen's Printer, Government of Newfoundland and Labrador.

Map: Newfoundland

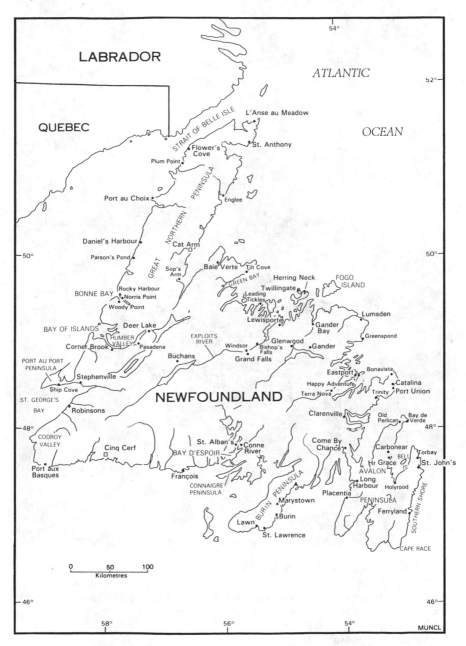

Cartography: Memorial University Cartographic Laboratory. Courtesy of Office of the Queen's Printer, Government of Newfoundland and Labrador.

Susannah Eveleigh was a "granny midwife," known throughout White Bay and the northeast coast of Newfoundland as "Aunt Susie." Without any formal education or training, she helped deliver more than 2,000 babies, all the while attending the sick and performing emergency medical services, as required.

Photo: Courtesy of Melvin Regular.

Introduction

Midwifery, one of the oldest female occupations, holds an obvious claim to the attention of anyone interested in the social history of women's work. During the past few decades midwifery has also attracted the notice of feminist writers concerned with the relationship between maternity care and female professional status. In the view of some feminist writers, the eclipse of traditional lay midwifery in the home environment and the subjection of birthing clients to male medical control in high-tech hospitals is but one example of the subordination of Western women as both occupational workers and clients (Rich 1975; Arms 1975; Ehrenreich and English 1979).

In attempting to conceptualise their findings, feminist writers have drawn upon two intertwined approaches to the study of health occupations—the thesis of a pervasive 'medicalisation' (Illich 1976; Zola 1972; Conrad and Schneider 1980; Willis 1983; Boehme 1984) of health service work in favour of medical specialists practising professional dominance (Freidson 1970), and the thesis of an increasing 'deprofessionalisation' of alternative health occupations in organisational settings (Johnson 1972; Larson 1977; Derber 1982; Toren 1975). Feminist writers adopting these interpretative frameworks have tended to depict midwifery in terms of an historical transformation of midwives from a situation of occupational autonomy and high status when lay midwives worked in clients' homes, to the present period of practice in large complex hospitals, characterised by patriarchal-medical dominance and deprofessionalisation (Oakley 1980; Rothman 1982; Greer 1984).

Yet, close attention to the premodern and present-day organisation of maternity care in comparative perspective calls into question the validity of this kind of analysis concerning the professionalism of midwives, an analysis that is almost exclusively based on American and British data. For comparative purposes, this book examines published research on the situation of midwives in Sweden, the Netherlands, Britain, the United States and central Canada. In addition, it draws on the author's own research on the organisation of midwifery in Canada's eastern-most province, Newfoundland and Labrador.

Newfoundland and Labrador provides a unique opportunity to test data from other areas of the West. For in Newfoundland and Labrador, the transition of midwifery services from home to bureaucratic settings was gradual rather than brisk. Lay midwifery continued in isolated communities into the post-World War II period, and some traditional homebirth attendants, known as 'granny women,' are still alive and available for interview. First-hand accounts of traditional midwifery provide a crucial 'reality test' of recent depictions of the childbearing patterns of our forebears. Furthermore, in contrast to most other places in North America where the occupation practically vanished as a result of modernisation, in Newfoundland and Labrador midwifery not only survived the shift from home to hospital but, equally unique, developed (in regions of the province still lodged in the historical space between tradition and modernity) a form of practice for midwives in small cottage hospitals which even today resists bureaucratisation.

With a notebook, an unstructured interview schedule and a portable tape-recorder as research tools, I began an investigation of midwifery in my home province. Travelling around the small coves and inlets of Newfoundland and northward to the Labrador frontier in order to interview and observe midwives at work brought me into contact with a territory and a people which were at once familiar and strange, stirring up long forgotten memories of my childhood outport life, which had become blurred by many years of urban residence. Preliminary analysis of my first encounters (based on field notes and tape-recorded life histories) with midwives from 'around the bay' and 'up the coast,' as locals refer to rural settlements of the province, indicated the importance which midwives place upon *sites of practice*. In their understanding, the site of practice was a crucial determinant of their freedom to organise work activities to their own liking as well as of their opportunity to acquire crucial maternity-care knowledge and, equally important, to forge satisfying relationships with the pregnant women placed under their care.

My initial respondents, grouped according to the sites of practice with which they had experience, fell into four overlapping types: (1) traditional homebirth attendants; (2) solo practitioners in rural clinics; (3) midwives employed in small cottage hospitals that flourished between the 1930s and 1960s but can now be found only in the northern areas of the province; and (4) rank-and-file workers in today's large regional hospitals, distinguished by state-of-the-art technology and a complex occupational hierarchy. A series of trips into the field eventually permitted me to interview additional mid-wives from each of the categories identified (for a total of 45 inter-views in all). These primary data were supplemented with field notes taken while observing midwives at work in health clinics, cottage hospitals and regional hospitals (observation did not take place in the home because homebirths today are exceptionally rare; the few births that still take place at home are usually the result of inclement weather preventing transportation to the hospital). Then came the laborious task of transcribing the many hours of interviews and field notes and searching the data for recurring themes. My initial find-ings were confirmed: over and over again my respondents indicated a deep concern not only with legal standing but also with issues of work autonomy and effective professional training and socialisation, all linked in their minds with the different structures of their occupational worlds. The vast majority of midwives in each of the four types agreed on one crucial point: compared with traditional granny women, with solo practitioners in rural clinics and with midwives working in present-day large bureaucratised hospital settings, only midwives in the small cottage hospitals approached the kind of secure occupational status desired by all.

This achievement of a considerable degree of professionalism by midwives in small organisational settings, dominated neither by community nor bureaucracy, calls into question much of the current sociological literature on the topic. It also has important policy implications for those Western countries presently attempting to reorganise their maternity-care systems and, in particular, for devel-oping societies contemplating changes in traditional birthing arrangements. In the pages which follow, Chapter 1 portrays a former cottage hospital midwife, Lou-Anne, before outlining major sociological perspectives on service work in late 20th century Western societies as well as describing the methods of research used in this book. Chapter 2 places the Newfoundland and Labrador case study in a wider context by offering a cross-national overview of midwifery practices in several other countries of the West. Succeed-ing chapters examine midwives' work worlds and styles of schooling and socialisation. The concluding chapter returns to the major theoretical positions examined in Chapter 1 and offers an alternative framework for understanding service occupations in historical and comparative perspective. The book concludes with an attempt to articulate some of the main policy issues emerging from the study.

Conceptualising Midwifery   1

PREVIEW: MIDWIFERY IN A NEWFOUNDLAND COTTAGE HOSPITAL

Lou-Anne,[1] a 57-year-old midwife, was born in Burgeo, a large fishing village on the southwest coast of Newfoundland, whose small cottage hospital, until recently, provided health care services to outport communities within a catchment area encompassing 60 miles of rugged coastline. Rapid modernisation, including construction of an unpaved highway in the early 1980s, ended the geographical isolation of Burgeo and neighbouring outports from the heartland of the province. As a result, Burgeo's status as the health centre for the southwest coast was lost. During the past two decades, a distant regional hospital (over 150 miles away) has become the dominant medical institution in the region, usurping most vital health services formerly carried out at the community level. Prior to these developments, Lou-Anne and her co-workers literally 'ran the show' on the cottage hospital maternity ward, and were held in high esteem by local birthing women[2] and their families.

Many traditional homebirth attendants, often referred to as 'handy women' or by the kinship terms 'auntie' and, more typically, 'granny,' also enjoyed high community status. Yet in other ways the two generations—traditional homebirth attendants and cottage hospital midwives—differed widely. The granny women received little or no formal education, instead garnering practical skills via informal apprenticeship and homebirth attendance. Lou-Anne, by contrast, is a *trained* midwife; in her view, acquisition of skills via practical experience and specialised formal knowledge of pregnancy and childbirth are both essential for qualified birth attendants. In addition, Lou-Anne stresses that she has always worked within a maternity division of labour. The granny women's solo practice in clients' homes without access to colleagues, doctors and life-saving technology, in fact, frightens her. Finally, Lou-Anne points out that her formal qualifications and practical experience resulted both in government licence and guaranteed salary, granting her the kind of security inaccessible to her granny forerunners.

Like many traditional lay midwives, Lou-Anne regards her work as a calling. Attending expectant mothers and their newborns, she notes, brings special reward:

> There is a great satisfaction in midwifery because it's a *happy* occasion. You see, it sort of tempered the other things in nursing, where you are looking after people who are very sick and probably burnt out and elderly—dying really. Then you get this young woman come in to have a baby and she's so happy. She has the baby and she's happier still. You know, its just such a happy occasion! It sort of levels things off. That's why I chose it.

In contrast to most of her occupational precursors, however, Lou-Anne wanted to undertake formal schooling in order to learn all there was to know about nursing and midwifery. Unlike her granny forerunners, who experienced only informal apprenticeship, Lou-Anne eventually received dual certification, seeking midwifery credentials after attaining her nursing diploma and working for a stint as a general ward nurse in her hometown cottage hospital. "The more I found out about maternity work, the more I decided I needed to become educated in this," she says. Her vocational midwifery training included extensive delivery experience and transmitted the latest obstetric techniques as well as the intention to serve all birthing clients, regardless of socio-economic and cultural background.

Cottage hospital practice gave Lou-Anne ready access to a secure work environment, and the relatively high birth rate (five or more children were typical then) provided her ample opportunity to keep her obstetric skills honed. Lou-Anne's midwifery activities entailed quite a challenge:

> What I didn't learn from the midwifery training, I could learn on the cottage hospital ward [because] we *had* to do these things, emergency things, including practical delivering of babies, with only the other midwife to help. We were around all the time, along with the cook and the janitor. A very small staff; there was no administrator and only occasionally a doctor. But we enjoyed it; it was a great life.

Despite the long hours (12-hour shifts were the norm) and the additional medical services demanded of cottage hospital midwives during the periodic absences of the resident doctor, work problems were relatively minor compared to the taxing situation of her lay forerunners, some of whom continued to provide emergency services to more isolated inhabitants even when the cottage hospitals were at their zenith. According to Lou-Anne, her government licence to practise, guaranteed salary, formal work schedule, cottage hospital setting and professional association were the envy of many granny midwives forced to toil around-the-clock, isolated from colleagues and back-up medical personnel, and often under extremely inadequate home conditions, for which they received meagre payment and sometimes nothing at all. Traditional lay midwifery was never a secure or enriching trade, in Lou-Anne's view, and became increasingly less attractive as conditions in the cottage hospitals improved in the post-World War II period.

Local clients, too, were pleased with the new style of midwifery offered at the Burgeo cottage hospital:[3]

> When I started work in Burgeo, the women came into the hospital. After the local granny midwife died, then the women were expected to come to the hospital and they just came. I think some of them really liked to come because, you know, it was quite a change. They were able to get away from a lot. Someone went in and took over their household while they were away. I guess it was a kind of holiday, or at least a rest.

Work in a setting which did not subject her to the watchful (and sometimes intrusive) surveillance of the community resulted in a level of occupational satisfaction for Lou-Anne and her cottage hospital co-workers that was rarely enjoyed by the grannies or their counterparts in rural clinics who had to endure the close monitoring of kin and neighbours. Nor did cottage hospital employment make Lou-Anne so minutely answerable to 'the powers that be'—staff physicians and administrators—as has become typical for her midwifery counterparts in today's large hospitals. Cottage hospital midwives and expectant mothers alike, in fact, were largely free from outside supervision. Moreover, the low level of medical technology at the Burgeo hospital meant that the midwife-client relationship was neither medicalised nor depersonalised. As Lou-Anne sums it up:

> To the women of Burgeo, coming into the cottage hospital to have a baby was like eating a piece of pie, you know. They wouldn't even know about this up-tightness common nowadays. Once in a while you'd get somebody, naturally, who was normally a nervous person. But they didn't have the concerns about it. They usually waited until they were just about ready to have the baby before they came

to the hospital, to tell you the truth! And they came in, had the baby and stayed in a few days and then went home. They all breast-fed if they could because we didn't bottle-feed in the hospital. And people were having an average of five or six children, so you got to know the mothers.

This unique organisation of maternity-care delivery, nicely balancing practitioner concerns and birthing client needs within a safe yet 'homey' hospital environment, has now become a fading memory, however, except for the northern areas of the province.[4] Lou-Anne's Burgeo workplace has managed to survive a little longer than other Island cottage hospitals, as a result of its remote location. But even Lou-Anne was recently forced to move to the provincial capital of St. John's, finding work in one of its referral hospitals. Despite her access to medical specialists and advanced obstetrical equipment, she contends that Newfoundland midwives have in many ways lost ground as a result of the dismantling of the cottage hospital system:

Now, these big hospitals—that's a horse of a different colour! You feel like you're in an assembly line. You can't say its this one's fault or that one's fault but the midwives are right in the middle of it. They're there; they listen to the woman. Then they're also on the other side, where the doctors are. It is very frustrating. The [social aspects] of health get run by the board...You see, having a baby is really a very natural thing but now things have gotten too *mechanical*, as far as I'm concerned. As soon as a woman comes into the big hospital, we hook her up to what they call a monitor. And there are so many doctors around. Its not the same anymore; you are no longer in control.

The cottage hospital midwife has enjoyed a degree of professionalism[5] available neither to her granny forerunners working on a fee-for-service basis in clients' homes nor to solo practitioners in rural clinics and nursing stations; it also remains unavailable today to her counterparts in large complex hospitals who are often reduced to the status, as one midwife puts it, of 'mechanical midwives.' This fact, however, does not correspond well with the major perspectives advanced by both popular writers and social scientists attempting to understand the place of service work in general, and midwifery in particular, in the occupational hierarchy. In the following pages, I briefly discuss three major approaches which have been brought to bear upon the study of midwifery before commenting upon the research methodology of this study.

SOCIOLOGICAL PERSPECTIVES ON HEALTH SERVICE WORK

The Medicalisation Thesis

The impetus behind feminist models of the alleged medical takeover of childbirth management in modern Western societies came from within medicine itself. In the 1940s a 'natural childbirth movement' emerged in North America, led by radical physicians alarmed by the increasing reliance upon drugs and techniques of physical intervention to intercede in the birth process. Perhaps the most prominent critic among them was the obstetrician Grantly Dick-Read, who argued that the expectant mother's pain in childbirth was not inevitable but rather the result of her fear and the tensing of her uterine muscles (Dick-Read 1944). According to Dick-Read, painful labour could be eliminated by proper relaxation and controlled breathing exercises, without having to resort to synthetic drugs.

Advocates of the natural childbirth movement were reacting against the then common practice of 'painless childbirth.' Originating in Germany in the early decades of the 20th century and promoted as a medical milestone for birthing women, the use of anaesthetics such as scopolamine[6] — popular for its 'twilight sleep' — soon became routine during normal childbirth in North America as well. Prominent clubwomen's associations pressured doctors into routine use of the drug, maintaining that twilight sleep would create a perfect motherhood, and that access to it would lead to the betterment of all of womankind (Leavitt 1980:154).[7]

At first glance, the natural childbirth movement seemed radical, since it called into question conventional medical wisdom and popular views of the day, including those of feminist activists who maintained that access to twilight sleep in medical settings gave parturient women greater control over the birth process than was the case during traditional homebirth. By adopting a more 'naturalistic approach' to labour and delivery, noted Dick-Read and his supporters, the problems resulting from the enormous variation in the use of scopolamine on hospital wards (i.e. its unpredictable timing through the labour process, and the non-standardised hospital conditions under which the drugged mother laboured) could be avoided altogether. Practice of the natural childbirth technique, it was argued, freed birthing women from dependency upon potentially dangerous chemical compounds, allowing them to remain awake during labour and to experience the joys of a successful delivery.

Elaborating on the natural childbirth approach, the French obstetrician, Fernand Lamaze, applied Pavlov's theories of the conditioned response to childbirth management and developed the 'psycho-prophylactic' method. In place of drugs, Lamaze advocated suggestion as a kind of 'verbal analgesia' in easing labour pains; the expectant mother remained conscious during the entire birthing process, following an elaborate, scheduled breathing drill for each stage (Lamaze 1955). More so than even the Dick-Read approach, the Lamaze method encouraged awareness and alertness; the pregnant woman was to respond to the obstetrician's verbal cues by panting, pushing and blowing.

Such alternative perspectives on childbirth management, while challenging the routine use of anaesthesia during the labour process, continued to leave much unquestioned. Both Dick-Read and Lamaze, though writing of 'painless' and 'natural' childbirth, took for granted an essentially male-dominated obstetrics practised in the context of a large teaching hospital. But, as later health commentators were to point out, birth attendants, birth technologies and birth settings, too, can significantly affect outcomes. In essence, the broader *structural* aspects of maternity-care delivery had yet to be called into question.

Subsequent feminist critiques of the natural and prepared childbirth movements have drawn upon a variety of supporting evidence, including anthropological studies of alternative maternal and childcare arrangements in non-Western societies. Soon after the end of World War II, female anthropologists provided evidence that the Western obstetrical model represents only one of many cultural forms; the ways of childbirth management in other cultures are numerous and varied (Mead 1949). Women's rite of passage through labour and delivery, they noted, is always embedded in particular beliefs, expectations, and customs, and remains in traditional cultures predominantly a *social* rather than a medical event (Ammar 1954; Mead and Newton 1967). Research on non-Western birthing practices have revealed that medical intervention is rare. Rather, expectant mothers are guided through their labour and delivery by village lay midwives, generally older women who have themselves borne children, sometimes receiving apprenticeship training prior to undertaking the role of homebirth attendant. Many are poor widows and thus unlikely to practise the kind of professional dominance characteristic of Western medical experts.

More recent feminist anthropological studies have highlighted the positive aspects of traditional lay midwifery for expectant mothers, who are able to give birth in their own homes or in an exclusive birth hut accessible to village kinswomen (Laderman 1983). In contrast to the potentially frightening and disorienting experience created by Western obstetrical practices for birthing

women isolated in an alien hospital environment, drugged throughout the labour process, monitored with elaborate equipment and
separated from their infants, anthropologists have found that in
small-scale societies the new mother and not the medical expert
remains the centre of attention. The village midwife does not hurry
her client or attempt to standardise the birth process; timing and
positioning during labour take place in accordance with the expectant mother's own wishes (Jordan 1983; Kitzinger 1972). Just as
importantly, the village lay midwives base their maternity practice
on local knowledge. Unlike the clinical hospital environment, the
homebirth setting helps to ensure that the midwife has an understanding of the life situations of her clients, which can facilitate
empathy concerning menopause (see Davis 1988).

Parallelling these research findings by anthropologists on family
and community centred maternity-care arrangements in small-
scale cultures, a women's health care movement began to emerge
both in Britain and North America in the early 1970s (see, for
example, the work of the Boston Women's Health Book Collective
1976). Movement activists have maintained that Western women
must regain control over all aspects of reproduction; they have
advocated a holistic health policy emphasising the *caring* dimension
and personal needs of women that have been largely neglected by
male experts of women's health.[8]

Central to the women's health-care movement in both the United
States and Canada has been childbirth management. Feminists
there have contended that, with or without analgesia, alert and
aware or drugged into semi-helplessness, North American birthing
women are essentially victims of male medical experts and intrusive
technology. The hierarchical structure of hospital maternity wards,
the dominance of staff physicians, the overarching view of pregnancy
and delivery as 'medical events' demanding emergency care have
resulted in fragmentation of the mother's psycho-social and biological needs. Medical dominance (Freidson 1970; Colburn *et al.* 1983)
is so extensive in North America, movement activists have claimed,
that obstetricians have virtually blocked other helping professionals, most of all midwives, from reaching out to pregnant women.
In their view, the medical bureaucracy, in all its guises, virtually
excludes women — attendants and clients — from active participation
in the most essentially female function of all, human reproduction.
As Rich (1975:26) puts it: "the loneliness, the sense of being in
prison, powerless and forgotten, is the chief collective experience of
women who have given birth in American hospitals." In brief, North
American feminists see modern motherhood as a contradictory

female life-event: from a woman's perspective, it is a positive experience; within the context of medico-bureaucratic control, however, it also becomes an oppressive institution (Bernard 1974; Arms 1975; Shaw 1974).

Disillusioned with North American practices, health critics turned their gaze to the other side of the Atlantic, hoping to discover there a way of avoiding the pitfalls of bureaucratic hospital obstetrics. Much to their surprise, they found large numbers of midwives at work within the British health services. At first glance, this would seem to indicate that male medical dominance is less prominent there, allowing for caring relationships between midwives and clients. Closer attention to the arrangement of British obstetrics, however, has left many North American feminists skeptical. The mere presence of midwives on obstetrical wards does not necessarily mean either that midwives in Britain enjoy professional standing[9] or that clients receive personalised care. Critics assert that the trend now well underway in Britain towards a bureaucratic organisation of maternity care and the consequent prominence of medical specialists in obstetrics has dethroned midwives and their clients from centre stage in the reproductive process, in much the same way as present-day North American obstetrical nurses have become alienated from the expectant mothers placed under their care (Kitzinger 1988). On both sides of the Atlantic, it seems, the hospital midwife's hands are now tied; she is powerless to remake birth into a 'woman's event' (Arms 1975). According to British sociologist Ann Oakley (1979:22), this should come as no surprise for "it is, after all, in the interests of a male-dominated society to play down the achievements of birth and lactation, and the connection with a woman's sexuality that these have."

Finding existing maternity-care arrangements everywhere wanting, feminists involved in the women's health care movement have begun to look to the past for enlightenment. Drawing upon a variety of secondary sources, including biographies, fiction and archival materials, they have rewritten the history of parturition in colonial America, frontier Canada and preindustrial Britain. Their focus upon the positive aspects of traditional lay midwifery has resulted in a demystification of the medical depiction of a 'dark age' of childbirth management prior to the emergence of modern obstetrics (Ehrenreich & English 1979; Oakley 1976; Wertz & Wertz 1977; Litoff 1978; Devitt 1979). These writers contend that the bleak picture presented by mainstream historians, who have charged traditional lay midwives with meddlesomeness[10] and even witchcraft (Forbes 1966), is a "sexist and professionalist Whig interpretation," written to glorify "the male-dominated present-day system of obstetric care" (Donnison 1981:38–9). In revising the historical records, feminist historians have arrived at a very different understanding of the midwives of the past, and some have even discovered a 'golden age'[11] of midwife-attended confinements. They contest that premodern midwives rarely intervened in the birth process, unlike the intrusive 'man-midwife' (as obstetricians were initially called) who dispossessed the traditional lay midwife and her homebirth clients of childbirth, placing it within a framework of pathology. As Scholten (1984:144) puts it: "in all circumstances the midwife's chief duty was to comfort the woman in labour while they both waited on nature." Oakley (1976:19) makes a similar claim concerning the entire domain of reproductive care:

> Childbirth, contraception and abortion are aspects of women's reproductive life. [T]hroughout most of human history it is women who have controlled their own reproductive function. That is, the management of reproduction has been restricted to women, and regarded as part of the feminine role...Women are the experts. Men are not involved, or are only marginally involved...Europe and America before industrialisation, and for some time after this, possessed indigenous female-controlled reproductive care systems.

Feminist historians have described a 'politics of midwifery' which took place in their respective countries between the late 1800s and the early decades of the 20th century (Kobrin 1966; Litoff 1986; Donnison 1977); they maintain that the elimination of the attractive lay midwife-homebirth alternative of the past and the subsequent 'medicalisation' (Conrad & Schneider 1980) of childbirth in the West has been based less on so-called objective science than on *patriarchy*—i.e., male control over female functions and, ultimately, male jealousy of women's generative powers (O'Brien 1981). Rich (1975:30) represents this historical reinterpretation in stating that medical men have 'stolen' childbirth from both female attendants and pregnant women:

> Patriarchal childbirth—childbirth as penance and as medical emergency—is alienated labour, exploited labour, keyed to the "efficiency" and a profit system having little to do with the needs of mothers and children, carried on in physical and mental circumstances over which the woman in labour has little or no control.

How can we recapture the positive features of childbirth experience taken for granted by our forebears? An alternative model, according to many feminists involved in the health-care movements on both sides of the Atlantic, can be found today in developing countries still relatively unaffected by Western medicine and its "impersonal conveyor-belt obstetrics" (Greer 1984:29). In their view, Western midwives, like their counterparts in still intact small-scale societies today, should be legally permitted to attend expectant mothers in clients' homes, beyond the reach of patriarchal and bureaucratic power (DeVries 1985; Eakins 1986). It has been further argued that in order to recapture the true art of midwifery, midwives must be free to train and socialise new recruits outside the dominant medical paradigm, via an informal apprenticeship system based on a woman-centred midwifery rather than a male-centred scientific model of reproduction (Rothman 1982).

In an attempt to place these findings on the medicalisation of midwifery within a broader theoretical framework, some feminist writers have drawn upon the sociological perspective that analyses the increasing 'deprofessionalisation' of non-elite service employees in post-industrial society.

The Deprofessionalisation Thesis

The pervasive medicalisation of maternity care by doctors utilising their extensive professional powers (Freidson 1986), some critics maintain, has 'deprofessionalised' Western midwives. Midwives, similar to other present-day service workers, it is argued, no longer possess the kind of professional freedom their forerunners enjoyed in solo practice, but are instead becoming mere 'mental labourers' clinging to an ever dwindling mandate (Derber 1982; Sorenson & Sorenson 1974; Larson 1977). To perform their routinised tasks effectively, midwives, like other non-elite occupational employees, are accountable to elite medical professionals and bureaucratic administrators, and at the same time dependent upon an ever more complex technology (Johnson 1972; Haug 1973).[12]

Some social critics have taken the deprofessionalisation thesis to its logical conclusion, maintaining that the growth of ever larger bureaucracies will eventually result in the full-scale proletarianisation of service workers, turning them into alienated labourers, a mere segment of the working class (concerning nursing, see Wagner 1980 and Warburton & Carroll 1988). Such writers suggest that a wide spectrum of social service employees is already experiencing the routinisation and rationalisation formerly typical only of industrial workers (Torrance 1987; Braverman 1974; Oppenheimer 1973). It has been claimed, as Marx argued over a century ago concerning factory workers, that advanced industrial capitalism leads to the increasing degradation of *all* non-elite service workers, mental and manual (Aronowitz 1973). This process involves not only a loss of autonomy but also a diminished opportunity to utilise unique esoteric knowledge and to develop sympathetic understanding of clients (Campbell 1984).

Many writers adopting these two intertwined theses—medicalisation and deprofessionalisation—conclude that the situation of service workers was quite different in the past. In their view, genuine professionalism for midwives and other non-elite service workers can be regained by a return to some form of informal apprenticeship training and solo practice; the ideal service professional, it is surmised, would be a new version of the independent lay midwife of the premodern era who practised in the local community, free from professional dominance and bureaucratic controls. Among present-day Western nations, the Netherlands is seen by social critics as an exception to the general pattern of professional medical dominance over childbirth, as the only country to uphold the age-old view of childbirth as a 'natural process' under the control of independent midwives working as homebirth attendants.

Yet, as will be shown in Chapter 2, examination of the actual situation of midwives in the Netherlands today calls into question the view that midwifery there is a truly independent profession. The Netherlands data reveal serious negative aspects accompanying homebirth attendance (some obstacles shared by traditional lay midwifery, others resulting from modern conditions of homebirth practice). These aspects typically have not appeared in the accounts of birthing arrangements in Western societies. By contrast, findings on present-day Sweden point to a greater level of professionalism for midwives in small health organisations. It is noteworthy that the findings on midwifery in these two countries closely reflect my own Newfoundland and Labrador data on midwifery in the home and small cottage hospital. They do not, however, support a third modern theory of service work—the professionalisation thesis.

The Professionalisation Thesis

Although agreeing that service employment in large complex organisations is characteristic of modern Western societies, advocates of the 'professionalisation thesis' have viewed this development as working for rather than against the professionalisation of occupational employees. In the opinion of these writers, some of whom, such as Freidson (1986), also adhere to the medicalisation thesis examined above, today's service organisations are based on professional not bureaucratic principles that enhance occupational autonomy and favour the utilisation of expertise for personalised care (Bell 1976). Some of the proponents of the professionalisation thesis have even contended that many contemporary service employees are members of a 'new class' (Gouldner 1978) or 'professional elite' (Freidson 1986) whose esoteric knowledge, advanced technical skills, legal authority and political association give them considerable power. Based on the premise that in late 20th-century Western society science and technology have emerged as the primary engines of economic growth, advocates of this line of reasoning have placed service employees rather than capitalists and state bureaucrats in the centre stage of power holding. These commentators have claimed that knowledge serves as a kind of 'cultural capital' through which professionals consolidate their supremacy in a complex division of labour (Galbraith 1967) and proceed to deploy pervasive 'technique' (Ellul 1980) or 'discipline' (Foucault 1979) in gaining control of nonprofessional staff and clients. According to professionalisation proponents, as industrial societies move towards a 'post-modern' stage of development, knowledge workers, male and female alike, will enjoy a degree of professionalism unavailable to their premodern counterparts in solo practice; they will form a 'new technocracy' (Bell 1980:144–64), usurping power from all sides in order to organise the delivery of social services around their own professional timetables.

While this theoretical model may enhance our understanding of, for example, medical specialists in large health science complexes with access to research institutes and legal institutions and backed by powerful professional associations, it fails to adequately conceptualise the situation of other service professionals, including rank-and-file medical practitioners in small organisations based upon a team approach. As writers adopting the intertwined medicalisation and deprofessionalisation theses would have predicted, the movement of Newfoundland and Labrador midwifery from cottage hospitals into larger, more complex institutions *has* entailed an erosion of the midwife's professionalism. This calls into question the professionalisation thesis that emphasises the relative freedom of service workers in determining terms and conditions of their occupational lives in bureaucratic settings. Research on the transition of family physicians and other non-elite professionals from solo practice and work in small organisations to bureaucratic sites of practice would be useful in testing my findings on midwifery.

Size of worksite, complexity of division of labour, and level of technology turn out to be decisive in the case of Newfoundland and Labrador midwifery: only in cottage hospitals were midwives able to realise their professionalism based on, among other things, freedom from community and medical-bureaucratic controls. Actual data supporting this principal finding will be presented in later chapters, and an alternative conceptual framework providing a better understanding of the situation of service workers in small organisations will be offered.

RESEARCH METHODS

This research project was not conceived *carte blanche* or in order to test some existing sociological theory. As is often the case in social research (Reinharz 1979; Zola 1983), my personal history played a significant role in the design and execution of this particular project. Born and reared a female and possessing the biological capacity to give birth, I was, it might be argued, not only more likely than a male researcher to be attracted to a study of past and present childbirth arrangements, but also to have an 'insider's knowledge' (Merton 1972) concerning this crucial female rite of passage. Moreover, I lived my preadolescent years in rural Newfoundland and have vivid memories of the local granny midwife—austere in appearance and never without a full white apron covering her ample bosom—making her rounds in my home community, including to my mother's bedside. As a curious teenager, I enjoyed the confidences of vacationing female kin, who related to me their fears and feelings of loneliness during confinements on anonymous maternity wards in the mainland Canadian cities where they had settled. My M.A. research, which involved a local community study of women in transition from a rural to an urban way of life, once again brought home to me the relevance of *birth setting*. While none of the women I interviewed had a desire for traditional homebirth attendance by granny midwives, almost all expressed deep remorse about the recent transformation of the local cottage hospital into a large regional health institution and the subsequent loss of status of both midwifery staff and birthing women (Benoit 1982).

I carried these overlapping interests—in midwifery and maternity care—on to graduate school in Toronto, where I proceeded to sharpen my limited formal knowledge through reading the growing body of writings on lay midwifery and childbirth practices in the preindustrial West as well as in present-day developing countries. Subsequent involvement in the emerging homebirth and midwifery movements in Toronto placed me in contact with a number of local lay midwives and some of the birthing women under their care. Utilising the biographical approach (Becker 1966; Langness and Frank 1981), I gathered, through open-ended interviewing, life histories of a small sample of these lay midwives and their homebirth clients. My major finding was a surprisingly strong disagreement among both groups of respondents concerning the ideal work site and means of educational guidance and socialisation for present-day midwives. This realisation inspired me to 'detach' myself from the immediate political struggle but nevertheless to remain 'involved' by embarking on research into this female service occupation in all its historical complexity (Elias 1956).

Choice of Setting

Research on traditional midwifery in modern-day Europe would yield only limited data: in most countries on the Continent as well as in Britain, it has long been eliminated. Without access to granny midwives for interview, it is not possible to examine living representatives of the historical roots of the occupation. On the other hand, a project designed to collect data on midwifery in present-day developing societies would provide only circumscribed data on midwifery practice predominantly in the home setting and on midwives' schooling and socialisation via informal apprenticeship.

Despite the overall marginality of midwifery in most areas of Canada and the United States, the Canadian province of New-foundland and Labrador provides a unique setting in which to examine the transformation of midwifery from its origins in the home, to the rural clinic, to the small cottage hospital, to, most recently, large-scale sites of practice.

Sample Process

The respondents interviewed were located by use of the 'snowball technique.' Although this sampling method has more often been used to locate marginal populations involved in illegal or morally questioned activities such as drug addiction, alcoholism, prostitution, and homosexuality (Becker 1963; Lindesmith 1968; Biernacki 1986), it can also be effectively used to start referral chains of service workers whose names do not appear on any official membership list or roll. Since the former Midwives' Roll has long been defunct and there exists no equivalent formal register of present-day midwives, random sampling was not a viable option in locating Newfoundland and Labrador midwives. Although more difficult to employ, the snowball technique eventually proved successful in securing an informal midwives' roster comprising respondents from the four overlapping types identified—traditional homebirth attendants; rural clinic midwives; cottage hospital midwives; midwives in large hospitals.

Initially, a small number of names of traditional lay midwives emerged from contact with local Women's Institutes and from researchers in Memorial University of Newfoundland's history and folklore departments. Informal conversations with key midwives involved in the nascent midwives' association started a referral chain of former clinic and cottage hospital midwives and their contemporary counterparts located in the capital city. From this preliminary sample, 12 midwives—a few from each category—were interviewed. Each of these respondents referred to other potential respondents, resulting in a list of approximately 70 retired and active midwives located throughout the province. Eventually 45 tape-recorded semi-structured interviews were carried out: eight with all the granny midwives known to survive in the province; 14 with an equal number of former and still active clinic and cottage hospital midwives, most of whom, in fact, had at some point worked in both sites of practice; and 23 interviews with a sample of midwives in today's large hospitals, many of whom had previously been employed in rural clinics and cottage hospitals. Interviews were also conducted with two former midwifery practitioners now working as health board administrators, four midwifery instructors at the university Nursing School and one male doctor who once practised side-by-side with midwives in a cottage hospital and presently serves as a resource person for information on such midwifery related topics as abnormal childbirth. A round-table discussion was launched with the entire midwifery class of 1985–1986, which yielded background information on the attending students, including their reasons for entering the program, their expectations upon graduation and so forth. In addition, observations were made of the activities of midwives and pregnant women and detailed field notes were written up: approximately 10 hours of observations in cottage hospitals, four hours in health clinics, and four hours in large regional hospitals. Moreover, periodic casual meetings occurred with the informal leader of the nascent midwives' association, who permitted perusal of and note taking from the written minutes of the association since its inception. The faded delivery books of three of the granny midwives interviewed, as well as the maternity records from one cottage hospital and one health centre, were scrutinised. Finally, permission was granted to attend an entire session of childbirth classes at a regional hospital and to take notes there.

Most shortcomings of this research procedure are common to all single-case studies using qualitative methods, especially concerning the problem of the generalisability of interview data (Hammond 1967). Problems resulting from 'interviewer bias' also arise—the communication between interviewer and interviewee, for example, may be distorted by mutual preconceptions (Glaser & Strauss 1967). The interviewer sometimes uses overly sophisticated jargon that is hardly accessible to respondents, thereby affecting the communication process. Although such problems can perhaps never be completely overcome, I hope that my own attempt to combine interviews with other types of qualitative (and, to some extent, quantitative) data, such as direct observation, informal conversations with key informants, attendance at meetings and classes, perusal of accessible documents, have all contributed to presenting the actual complexity of the transformation of Newfoundland and Labrador midwifery.

Interview Schedule

The first phase of fieldwork and unstructured tape-recorded interviews with midwives of diverse career paths revealed some interesting data. One surprising finding was a consensus among traditional lay midwives that, rather than inter-professional rivalry with travelling male doctors, it was the gradual modernisation of their outport communities, accompanied as it was by the availability of a small number of rural clinics and, more significantly, by a cottage hospital system employing an impressive work force of vocationally-trained midwives, that led to the eventual demise of homebirth practice in the aftermath of World War II. It furthermore became clear from these preliminary interviews that traditional lay midwives embraced neither the anti-hospital slant found in the feminist and deprofessionalisation literatures nor the implicit assumption among professionalisation theorists that midwives enjoy professionalism in complex hospital settings. Rather, all grannies were of the opinion that the small cottage hospitals, and not clients' homes, rural clinics or large hospitals, were ideal meeting grounds for both midwives and parturient women. Likewise, analysis of the interviews with former and still active rural clinic, cottage hospital and regional and referral hospital midwives in the preliminary sample indicated that they, too, were in agreement with their traditional lay counterparts concerning the crucial importance of the cottage hospitals in midwives' achievement of professionalism.

Interviews carried out during subsequent trips into the field were semi-structured. In addition to biographical and community data and information on clientele, a set of guiding questions highlighting the positive and negative characteristics of different patterns of midwifery education, socialisation and practice formed the core of the interview schedule (see Appendix I). Even at this advanced stage, interviews were intentionally left open-ended, allowing for flexibility in discovering potential lines of consensus and dissensus among the different categories of midwives. Most interviews were conducted in respondents' homes, which involved travel to outport and larger communities in both Newfoundland and Labrador. Because of work restraints or preference for privacy away from family, a few respondents chose to be interviewed in their place of employment, providing useful information on working conditions, including time schedules, collegial relations and situation of birthing clients. In determining the number of midwives to interview, the theoretical saturation method was used (Glaser & Strauss 1967:61–2). As the interviewing progress neared termination, it became clear that no new data of significance were emerging from the interviews.

The interviews ranged from roughly one to three hours in length and a number of interviews were repeated, some a third time, in order to gain additional information. All interviews were transcribed and coded. Prior to the interview, respondents were informed about the purpose of the study and assured that their identities would be kept strictly confidential. The interviews were carried out exclusively by myself. My gender, no doubt, facilitated a relatively smooth entrance into the field (Warren 1988), and my status as one of 11 children of Newfoundland parents helped establish rapport with older respondents in particular. Whenever possible, I tried to adjust my patois and orientation to that of the midwives themselves. Although this strategy did not remove all tension from the interview process, most respondents relaxed after the initial encounter and remained open throughout.

Only two midwives refused to be interviewed. A granny midwife contacted by phone declined an interview. She maintained that her memories of midwifery had all but faded and that "it would not be very nice to call them back." Another midwife, a single parent of two young children working nights in a large regional hospital, also rejected my request for an interview, legitimately protesting that she simply did not have a spare moment. Apart from these two exceptions, my interviewees were generally delighted at the opportunity to reflect upon their own careers and comment upon the changing situation of midwifery.

Typology of Newfoundland and Labrador Midwives

All midwives in the study have the same sex status and claim the occupational title of midwife. Nevertheless, they can be divided into

four overlapping types—traditional lay midwives, rural clinic midwives, cottage hospital midwives and ward practitioners in large
hospitals—reflecting the historical transformation of their occupation. These four types are systematically associated with a number
of characteristics, including the size of the descriptive population,
social class, immigrant status, age, work experience, level of
specialisation, educational credentials and career orientation.

No traditional lay midwives practise today, and most of those
who practised in the past are no longer alive. I was forced to search
for a composite picture of the typical granny woman by interviewing
the eight survivors. The traditional lay midwife was a many-faceted
service worker. In addition to assisting neighbouring women in
childbirth and providing help and advice for problems related to
sexuality and reproduction throughout the female life cycle, she
served as a lay healer for all local people during times of illness.
Moreover, she often schooled trainees via an informal apprenticeship system.

Although no reliable statistics exist for any category of midwife,
the actual number of traditional lay midwives, considering that
many of the over 5,000 outport settlements as well as most urban
pockets had at one time or other at least one granny midwife, was
relatively large in comparison to both the later cottage hospital
midwives and their counterparts in regional and referral hospitals.
The vast majority of granny women, usually of peasant or working
class background, were married and had large families (seven or
more children were not uncommon). The poorest among them were
widowed and often undertook midwifery because it was the only paid
work available to women. Rarely did the granny women have public
schooling beyond the third grade, and only a few had any formal
nursing or midwifery training. By and large they 'picked up' their
midwifery and healing skills through an informal system of apprenticeship and homebirth practice. The granny women usually
practised in their place of birth or in a nearby settlement. In a very
real sense, then, they were community midwives. While some granny midwives claimed to have been 'called' to their work, the majority
'fell into' the role of midwife because nobody else was available to
perform such essential service functions and because no other
livelihood was available to them.

While the benefits to outport women of the personalised care
provided by granny midwives in their own home communities were
of great importance, the disadvantages of high maternal and infant
morbidity and mortality must not be overlooked.[13] Beginning in the
early 1920s, local health authorities attempted to improve birth

outcomes by establishing the 'Newfoundland Outport Nursing and Industrial Association' (NONIA), which introduced the first vocation-ally-trained nurse-midwives to isolated settlements along the Island's rugged coastline. Most of the new generation of midwives were recruits from the British Isles. However, among them were also local graduates who had travelled to the capital city of St. John's and enrolled in one of the midwifery courses getting underway at that time (see footnote 15 on page 134). A few others were Island women who had sought nurse-midwifery training abroad. While the Board of Health contributed some starting grants and helped the poorest communities to initially pay salaries, it was expected that in the long run the outport settlements themselves would build clinics and raise funds to sustain them. Outport Committees were set up for this purpose and 'knitting circles,' 'weaving bees' and similar cottage industry ventures were launched; community women freely contributed their time and skill to produce quality crafts, the payment for which would go towards the upkeep and salary of the NONIA midwife in their employ.

Nevertheless, recruitment to the Outport Scheme was not a great success, not least because of the heavy demands made on the new employees. In fact, even the Health Department cautioned that 'care be taken to select locations where the nurse-midwife would have access to a clergyman or Justice of the Peace who would make it his duty to see that she was not overworked' (Nevitt 1978:128). Most NONIA nurse-midwives remained transients, however, their rapid turnover resulting from heavy work loads, shortage of supplies, isolation from emergency medical facilities, and high expectations of a needy population previously dependent exclusively upon the local granny woman to meet their many health care needs. By 1933, after barely a decade of operation, the number of NONIA clinics had dwindled from 25 to eight (Nevitt 1978:224). The last NONIA mid-wives, in fact, became the first employees of the new Cottage Hospital System.

The Cottage Hospital System, based on the Highland and Islands hospital scheme then operating in Scotland's far north, comprised 18 small organisations strategically located in the larger New-foundland towns outside the two major urban areas—St. John's on the east coast and Corner Brook on the west coast—both providing specialised care in general hospitals with sizable maternity wards and obstetrical teams. In the northern part of the Island and in Labrador, cottage hospitals were constructed by the philanthropic Grenfell Association. These half-dozen small organisations were gradually modernised and a few were moved to adjacent sites in

accordance with changing population patterns. The others continued to serve normal maternity clients in their catchment areas
until they were dissolved in the early 1970s.[14]

The new Cottage Hospital System was able to remedy many of
the shortcomings of maternity care in both home and rural clinic.
The result was a gradual shift from childbirth in peripheral locations
to midwifery attendance in cottage hospitals located in adjacent
towns, and from an informal apprenticeship system to formal training and certification of regional women interested in nurse-
midwifery as a full-time career. Whereas elsewhere in North America
midwifery was rapidly eliminated by way of the bureaucratic organisation and medical dominance of maternity care (Biggs 1983;
Wertz and Wertz 1977), in Newfoundland and Labrador it was
gradually transformed, comparable to contemporaneous developments in Sweden (see Chapter 2), where midwifery-staffed
'mothercare centres' opened in the 1930s and continue even today
to provide free care to maternity clients experiencing normal
deliveries (Seward, Seward and Natoli 1984). This development
created a space in the evolving maternity division of labour for a new
category of relatively autonomous trained midwife.

Who were the midwives employed in these emerging cottage
hospitals? The first local recruits, from both Newfoundland and
Labrador communities, comprised a small number of older experienced granny women as well as younger aspirants without
apprenticeship training or homebirth experience. Although this was
less true for the grannies, their youthful counterparts typically
attained nursing credentials, in addition to specialised midwifery
training, either in a three-month course given by the Midwives' Club
established in the mid-1920s or in an integrated 'maternity nursing
course,' both in the capital city of St. John's (Nevitt 1978).[15] Not all
of the midwives employed in the cottage hospital system were
native-born, however. British migrant midwives or, to use a present-
day term, 'guest workers,' many of whom had worked in isolated
NONIA clinics or in nursing stations in the Canadian North, were
also among them. A number of cottage hospital midwives—come-
from-aways (CFAs) as well as locals —married into the towns where
their workplace was situated, typically leaving the workforce during
early motherhood but eventually resuming their careers, often as
ward supervisors. Such longterm government employment resulted
in an incremental rise in economic standing for cottage hospital
midwives, placing them on a rough par with other service workers,
such as school teachers, social workers, and post office attendants.
though there exist no published statistics on midwives employed

in the regional and referral hospitals that succeeded the cottage hospital system, a composite picture of this small group can easily be drawn up by way of interviewing informants. Today's 15 regional and referral hospitals typically employ one or, at most, two midwives on their maternity wards, with some employing none at all. After a short period of maternity work, many regional and referral hospital midwives move on to nursing administration or teaching. They do not constitute a homogeneous group: their socio-economic standing differs widely, depending on family circumstances and employee status. Much depends upon their marital situation (single mothers maintaining a household on one income vs being a partner in a dual-career family) and career line (ward practice, administration, teaching). Furthermore, regional and referral hospital midwives' occupational preparation differs considerably from that of their forerunners. The typical granny had no formal education. Regional and referral hospital midwives, like rural clinic and cottage hospital practitioners, have at least a high school diploma, in addition to specialised nursing and maternity training; an increasing number are baccalaureate degree holders from university nursing schools, with only limited practical experience, in comparison to the extensive bedside and community experience required by the now defunct vocational midwifery program. While this kind of occupational socialisation is more typical for native-born recruits, many midwives who belong to the category of 'imported labour' desiring landed immigrant status, are now on the 'academic bandwagon'; improving their vocational credentials by acquiring a university degree increases their opportunity to eventually attain Canadian resident status.

Not surprisingly, the recent transformation of the training and practice of midwifery has been accompanied by shifts in career orientation. Unlike cottage hospital midwives who tend to articulate an inner calling for their maternity work, few regional and referral hospital midwives speak spontaneously of a dedication to the service of pregnant women and their families. Nor do they plan life-long careers as midwifery practitioners. Local and immigrant midwives differ little in this regard, both viewing bedside midwifery as a mere stepping stone in their careers. Many immigrant midwives in regional and referral hospitals plan to return home after a year or two, unless they are able to secure work in a metropolitan area. Similarly, local recruits tend to view midwifery merely as a fall-back option, as a 'good certificate to have'; many, in fact, do not plan to work as midwives at all.

SUMMARY

The historical shift of Newfoundland and Labrador midwifery from home to rural clinic, small cottage hospital, and eventually to bureaucratic site is not easily explained by either of the three sociological models—medicalisation, deprofessionalisation, professionalisation—that attempt to understand the position of health service work in late 20th century societies. Presentation of my findings on midwives' work worlds (Chapter 3) and styles of instruction and socialisation (Chapter 4) will be preceded by a cross-national investigation of midwifery in several Western countries. This investigation will show that the historical trajectory of Newfoundland and Labrador midwifery has not been entirely unique.

Midwifery in Cross-National Perspective   2

*As a biological event [birth] is 'universal' among human groups, yet
its practices in different societies show considerable diversity.*
                                               Callaway 1978:163.

Maternity-care arrangements in the present-day world may be
broadly divided between those in which adequate access to scientific
medicine prevails (as in advanced industrial countries), and those
in which limited or even no access to medical specialists and high
technology exists (as in most Third World countries). Like premodern Europe and colonial North America, many developing and
underdeveloped countries continue to rely almost exclusively upon
community healers, usually lay midwives, to attend parturient
women in their own homes or in a special ritual hut (Greer 1984).

Despite its considerable social and psychological advantages for
clients, homebirth attendance by traditional lay midwives, in the
present as much as in the past, has been beset with high infant and
maternal mortality rates. It is, therefore, not surprising that this
original form of maternity care became the focus of public debate in
the West during its early industrial period, and that it is now a
central concern (along with poor nutrition and inadequate housing)
of those less-affluent countries' in the Third World which have
embarked upon the path of economic and social development.

Throughout the 19th and early 20th centuries, Western govern-
ments on both sides of the Atlantic undertook a variety of pronatalist policies in an attempt 'to save mothers and babies' (Donnison 1977; Buckley 1979). At the same time, public access to safe
birth control and abortion was expanded, thereby helping to ease
the physical and emotional strains accompanying frequent child-

bearing (Gordon 1976; McLaren & McLaren 1986). Whereas in
medieval Europe, for example, seven or more pregnancies per
woman were not uncommon, by the mid-20th century comparable
figures had fallen to less than half this number, and proceeded to
fall further in succeeding decades (Wrigley 1969). In brief, this dual
development—improved maternity-care facilities and reproductive
control—has greatly helped to make childbirth a *choice* rather than
the destiny of many modern women (though significant lags still
persist among racial and ethnic minorities and the economically
disadvantaged).

The Western path toward the goal of voluntary motherhood has
not been without unwanted side effects, however. In the past few
decades there has been a profusion of literature, in both Britain and
North America, about women's reproductive role, particularly
regarding the psychosocial aspects of this key life role. According to
health activists, over-reliance upon scientific medicine can have
undesirable psychological and sometimes physical consequences
for newborns and mothers, placing them, like their counterparts in
developing countries, 'at risk,' although for very different reasons.
Feminist writers have found that women who experience normal
pregnancies but are deprived of active participation in the birth
process report contradictory feelings of joy and anxiety and fear
concerning their labours and deliveries (Shaw 1974; Rothman 1982;
Oakley 1980), and some writers have even maintained that mother-
child relationships are detrimentally affected (Klaus and Kennell
1976; Rossi 1977).

Maternity care in Europe (with the exception of the Netherlands)
and North America, health activists suggest, has fallen prey, like
other human mental and physical processes, to pervasive medicalisation (Illich 1976; Zola 1972; Conrad & Schneider 1980; Boehme
1984) and midwives, like most other health attendants, have experienced subordination by a patriarchal medical elite practising
professional dominance (Freidson 1970; Willis 1983; Betz & O'-
Connell 1983). In the picture they have painted, midwifery appears
to have travelled a relatively straight path from a Golden Age of
occupational autonomy, during which traditional lay midwives
worked in their clients' homes, to the present period of hospital-
based practice, characterised by a loss of their earlier freedom,
medicalisation and deprofessionalisation (Oakley 1980; Rothman
1982; Greer 1984).

Close attention to the diverse historical and contemporary arrangements of reproductive care reveals the limited explanatory
value of the overlapping medicalisation and deprofessionalisation

theses as well as of the contrasting professionalisation thesis, which associates high occupational status with large sites of occupational employment. Cross-national analysis of existing data, in fact, points to a significant *heterogeneity* rather than homogeneity of place of birth and primary attendant across and even within nation-state boundaries. Comparative findings reveal some negative aspects accompanying homebirth attendance, aspects which typically have not appeared in the accounts of birthing arrangements in Western societies. These data also support the contention that the organisation of maternity care in small health organisations is, in fact, a development that is advantageous for clients, and at the same time results in substantial occupational power for the midwifery occupation.

This chapter discusses the work situation of midwives in a limited number of Western nations: Sweden, the Netherlands, Britain, the United States and Canada. Midwives' present-day occupational standing can be arranged along a continuum from comparatively high status in Sweden to low status in many areas of the U.S. and most of Canada, with Dutch and British midwives falling somewhere in-between the extremes.

SWEDEN

Midwifery in Sweden has developed a level of occupational autonomy not found in other developed nations. An elaborate maternity-care arrangement along social democratic principles contributes to widespread client satisfaction and provides a privileged occupational status to Swedish midwives.

As in most other Western countries, childbirth in Sweden was traditionally a restricted family event (Seward *et al.* 1984). Care of mother and newborn was in the hands of a designated lay member of the local community—typically a female midwife—who was sometimes assisted by kin and neighbours in clients' homes or in small private delivery units located in apartment buildings. As late as in the 1920s, few hospitals, except in the largest cities, contained maternity wards. Yet despite the advantages of the non-hospital environment for some Swedish women (those with adequate housing and able to afford private services), infant mortality remained high, with rates between 55 and 65 deaths per 1,000 live births (Rooth 1979:1170).

By the late 1930s, however, Sweden had passed through a relatively speedy planned transition to modernisation, under the auspices of a strong welfare state. Of primary concern was the quality of maternal and child care. A parliamentary commission called for the radical transformation of the traditional midwifery services still based on fee-for-service practice in private domiciles. This approach was replaced by a modern maternity-care system comprising three major components: (1) free and comprehensive assistance to all birthing women and their newborns; (2) construction of a three-tiered hospital system organised around a midwifery rather than a medical model of care; and (3) collection of extensive population statistics (Myrdal and Myrdal 1945). These efforts culminated in a national birth registration which today includes the medical history of each maternity case from the onset of prenatal care through delivery and into the postnatal period.

Sweden's novel approach to modernising traditional midwifery provided its female citizens, regardless of social class, geographical location, ethnicity, religious affiliation and political persuasion, with a wide choice of both attendant and place of birth. At the same time, women's safety and comfort during childbearing have been significantly improved. One measurable result is greatly reduced mortality figures. In the past five decades, the country's infant mortality rate has decreased uniformly among all social groups, falling to a rate of eight deaths per thousand births in 1976, approximately one-seventh the figure recorded prior to the institutionalisation of the modern system. The rate had dropped further to seven per thousand births by 1980 (Seward 1984:11). Today Sweden enjoys the lowest infant mortality rate in the world. Maternal death rates took an even greater plunge in the modern period, and now rarely appear in population statistics (Tomasson 1970).

A second, less quantifiable but equally important result has been consistent reporting of high emotional satisfaction concerning their maternity care by present-day Swedish women. Although there is ready access to specialists and high-tech medicine, parturition in Sweden has not become an overwhelmingly medical event in which the pregnant woman is transformed into a sick person or 'patient' (Parsons 1951), rendered helpless in the face of the obstetrical problem at hand. Rather, the modernisation of Swedish maternity care has led to a conceptualisation of childbirth as "an intensely personal, fulfilling achievement" (Jordan 1983:34). Swedish families are provided with extensive social services that help to make the transition to parenthood an *individual* choice, with medical and technological forms of outside control held at bay. In order to enhance personal choice regarding parenthood, both birth control and abortion are legal and freely available to all women, resulting in the vast majority of births being both wanted and planned. Not surprisingly, Sweden now has one of the world's lowest birth rates.

Along with extensive reproductive freedom has come the organisation of a maternity-care system based upon an independent and strong midwifery occupation. Client care during pregnancy and childbirth falls under the jurisdiction of the Swedish National Board of Health and is free of charge. In contrast to other Western countries where the bureaucratisation of parturient care has resulted in increasingly more births taking place in ever fewer huge hospitals, very large obstetrical wards are rare in Sweden, and are utilised for high risk care only. Swedish maternity care is rather organised along a *decentralised* plan, where midwives coordinate the care of all birthing clients, referring only abnormal cases to more centralised levels of care.

The linchpin of this multi-level maternity system is the Swedish midwife's principal work site—the 'local mothercare centre.' These small maternity units are strategically located in towns and in the few large cities. Uppsala, for example, with a population of 100,000, operates 10 mothercare centres (Rooth 1979:1171). Such an economically efficient provision of midwifery services has the added advantage that clients receive care close to home. The local neighbourhood mothercare centres, referred to as 'Type-I Clinics,' are staffed by government-employed nurse-midwives who dispense pre- and postnatal care, and perform all normal deliveries within their catchment area. Both health administrators and the public at large view the Swedish midwife as a highly trained expert capable of diagnosing, for example, signs of abnormality. Such special cases are referred to a general practitioner at a 'Type-II Clinic.' If a serious gynecological problem is discovered, the general practitioner proceeds to transfer the client, now viewed as at risk, to a 'Type-III Clinic.' Only at this point does the birthing woman find herself in the role of obstetric patient. This highly coordinated system of maternity care in present-day Sweden provides a screening process that "separates normal from potentially complicational pregnancies and assigns each to their appropriate environment" (Jordan 1983:41).

At the same time, a relatively straight career path is available to Swedish midwives, permitting high occupational standing. Essentially working as autonomous employees in the neighbourhood mothercare centres, midwives serve as a solid counterbalance to the tendency of the obstetrical profession in most Western countries to medicalise normal childbirth and to make it their own domain—for example, by placing childbirth in the setting of a high-tech teaching hospital (Seward *et al.* 1984). Swedish midwives in the mothercare centres act as *first points of contact* for all clients, using their own discretion in deciding whether a particular woman is in need of obstetrical intervention. Physicians are thereby forced backstage, moving to the forefront only for clients in danger, and possibly also for those in need of exceptional treatment.

Swedish women can experience their passage through pregnancy and childbirth as their own personal achievement; the *midwife*, not a doctor, acts as their guide. The mothercare centres are designed to provide a homelike setting for labour and delivery without the trappings of a sterile operating room, welcoming the father's direct involvement in the birth process, encouraging rooming-in, setting aside visiting hours for older children and friends and, perhaps most importantly, providing frequent and continuous care from the same staff midwife whenever possible. It is therefore hardly surprising that homebirth and lay midwifery movements have not emerged in Sweden. This itself indicates satisfaction—among midwives and clients alike—with the existing perinatal services available as part of the government-funded national health care system.

The Swedish case, in effect, shows that the erosion of homebirth and independent lay midwifery does not inevitably lead to either medicalisation of childbirth or the subordination of female birth attendants by a powerful male medical elite. Provided maternity-care services are socialised, organisational scale is controlled, and midwives are awarded a primary role in the health division of labour, small maternity hospitals may actually *enhance* their occupational power.

THE NETHERLANDS

Although similar to Sweden in regard to the legalisation of midwifery practice, the maternity division of labour in the present-day Netherlands differs from that of its northern neighbour in crucial ways. Two features in particular—midwives' worksite in the homes of clients and mode of reimbursement based on fee-for-service—indicate that even now the Netherlands share much in common with traditional forms of maternity-care delivery.

While in Sweden modernisation has been accompanied by the development of a socialised health-care system, including an elaborate arrangement of federally-financed maternity clinics staffed by trained midwives, in the Netherlands crucial aspects of the traditional maternity-care system based on independent midwifery practice have been retained, with institutionalised practice complementing rather than replacing homebirth attendance. The modern-day Netherlands health insurance system, in fact, does not cover clients' hospital labour and delivery expenses unless serious medical complications are predicted by the attending midwife or general practitioner. While greater knowledge of obstetrical emergencies has increased the referral rate, more than one-third of all babies are still born at home (Phaff 1986:117).

Impressive perinatal and maternal mortality outcomes indicate that, at least at the statistical level, the homebirth system of the Netherlands does not detract from high-quality maternity care. Extensive prenatal examinations of pregnant women for possible obstetrical problems no doubt contribute to the low mortality rates. Furthermore, the country's relatively small geographical area and efficient transportation system put most clients within easy reach of specialised obstetrical facilities (Damstra-Wijmenja 1984).

Apart from the popularity of homebirth, the Netherlands also differs from Sweden regarding reimbursement of midwifery services. Just like general practitioners and other helping professionals involved in maternity-care delivery, midwives in the Netherlands are remunerated on a fee-for-service basis. The majority of midwives work as independent entrepreneurs and are legally permitted to supervise normal deliveries without medical surveillance. Upon finding themselves pregnant, clients normally choose a free-lance midwife who carries them through the prenatal, delivery and post-partum periods. The midwife is paid the prevailing health insurance rate for the services rendered.

The beneficial side of this form of maternity care based on fee-for-service homebirth attendance is that it permits family-centered childbirth. Risks of infection, restrictive rules and regulations, 'daylight obstetrics' (premature induction of women in labour to fit the doctor's nine-to-five weekday timetable), and unnecessary use of obstetrical forceps and Caesarian section—all common in large medically-dominated bureaucratic hospitals—are thereby avoided. Home and family continue to provide a protective boundary for pregnant women, and many clients can experience birth as a 'natural' event (Jordan 1983:36–7). Attention by a single primary care giver also reduces the likelihood that birthing women will be pushed along a system of 'conveyer-belt obstetrics' (Rothman 1982), which is presently the case in many high-tech teaching hospitals where 'professional strangers' divide the reproductive process among themselves, leaving the birthing woman out of the picture altogether (Shaw 1974).

The maternity-care system in the Netherlands based on home-birth has some unfortunate consequences for both midwives and clients, however. Fee-for-service midwifery in the home setting does not necessarily lead to occupational autonomy for birth attendants. Although midwives working outside an organised division of labour enjoy freedom from bureaucratic administrators and medical specialists, their situation is hardly unfettered by external pressures. Not unlike traditional birth attendants in Third World societies, midwives in solo practice who rely upon midwifery as a primary source of income are, in the Netherlands, often caught in the age-old paradox affecting all non-salaried service practitioners: they need to run a successful business while also providing family-centered care to their homebirth clientele. Their plight is shared by U.S. lay midwives. As one of them puts it:

> It's hard to go for years and years without making money...I have done it and I am tired of it... I am a single mother and I have the responsibilities of keeping my phone paid, and my beeper paid, and my paper work up, and my car going and my kid fed...I try to be as business-like as I can and still keep in touch with their spiritual, psychological, financial, health kind of needs and that's hard to balance" (quoted in Weitz and Sullivan 1985:47).

With no guaranteed salary to help meet monthly overhead costs and daily subsistence needs, midwives in independent practice must be 'on call' in the Netherlands 24 hours every day, making other part-time employment virtually impossible. The only way for a midwife to earn a reasonably comfortable income is to enter into competition with other homebirth attendants in an attempt to increase her client load. But such a business strategy often leads to new problems, not least that of managing increased demand for the midwife's scarce time. One way of avoiding this situation is for the midwife to limit the amount of time spent with each client. However, the likely result of this course of action is a standardised and routinised care quite different from the ideal image of midwifery based on a notion of *partnership* between midwife and pregnant woman (Oakley 1980; Rothman 1982).

The balance between earning a profit from services rendered and commitment to client-centered midwifery is thus not easily achieved by midwives in the Netherlands. Recent reports suggest that some free-lance midwives have gone so far as to delay the referral of needy clients for special tests, based on the realistic fear of loss of income should the obstetrician recommend medical treatment and hospital delivery (Phaff 1986). There is also the problem of gaining access to an appropriate number of clients in order to keep delivery skills honed. An oversupply of general practitioners and obstetricians in the Netherlands also on fee-for-service pay schedules has resulted in increased competition for maternity clients—particularly economically advantaged pregnant women willing to pay privately for medical services—precisely at a time when the birth rate has dropped to an all-time low of about 1.5 children per woman. Unlike their Swedish counterparts in the mothercare centres, where a steady supply of maternity clients provides a unique opportunity to use specialised midwifery knowledge and technical skills on a daily basis, midwives in solo practice in the Netherlands must cope with an 'open market' situation, which often results in too few or too many clients at any one point in time (Teijlingen & McCaffery 1987).

A further interference with the occupational autonomy of Netherlands midwives is their separation from colleagues. With the home as her work world, the midwife must make decisions in isolation from peers. Her Swedish counterparts are able to avoid this unattractive situation since they are part of a midwifery *team* in the mothercare centres.

One final observation should be made in regard to the Netherlands' system based on independent midwifery. Given the absence of a career ladder in homebirth attendance, a midwife no longer able to cope with the rigours of solo practice has little choice but to retire altogether. Her Swedish counterparts, by contrast, have the option of seeking managerial positions in the local mothercare centres, overseeing the work of youthful colleagues and transmitting to them the special skills unique to their occupation. Midwives working in solo practice in the Netherlands are without this opportunity for career advancement; many experience occupational blockage or 'burnout' after a stint of homebirth attendance.

In sum, the organisation of maternity care in the present-day Netherlands, still largely based on traditional homebirth attendance and fee-for-service reimbursement, enhances midwives' occupational power to a limited extent only. The midwife's work is circumscribed in many ways, not least regarding uncertain economic return for services rendered in clients' homes, around-the-clock work schedule, and unpredictable caseload. Isolation from like-minded colleagues leaves her stressed when facing difficult decisions concerning obstetrical risk without access to a second opinion. Furthermore, absence of career mobility often results in premature retirement. Opportunity for employment in small government-funded maternity units, such as the Swedish mothercare centres, might help ease these structural problems, and possibly grant midwives a measure of control over their occupational lives that remains impossible as long as present conditions of practice prevail.

BRITAIN

Like Sweden and the Netherlands, premodern Britain, too, depended upon the ancient institution of lay midwifery to carry women through the reproductive process. Originally midwifery there was practised as a form of mutual support among women in village communities (Donnison 1977). This system remained intact in most of Britain until comparatively recently; 'wise women' (analogous to the French *sage-femmes*), chosen on the basis of high moral character and practical knowledge of pregnancy and childbirth, were 'elected' to the office of midwife by the villagers (Boehme 1984:371). In the final analysis, however, the local clergy was vested with the power to discipline any member of the midwifery occupation whose behaviour deviated from church principles (Donnison 1977:7).

In the mid-19th century, the structure of traditional British midwifery began to be undermined, paralleling the incipient modernisation of other service occupations (Ackerknecht and Fisher-Homberger 1977). Midwives were finally granted state licence by the turn of the 20th century, but only after persistent politicking by a multiplicity of parties: prominent midwives themselves, young middle-class women desiring a viable career option outside of marriage and motherhood, obstetricians and elite general practitioners who could afford not to worry about economic competition from midwives, and affluent female philanthropists who viewed the well trained midwife as the safest and cheapest attendant of their less fortunate working-class sisters (Donnison 1981:7–8). The concerted efforts of these various groups calling for midwifery reform ultimately proved successful, resulting in the Midwives' Act of 1902. Subsequent generations of British midwives enjoyed nationwide recognition and licensing through their own Central Midwives' Board. These changes granted British midwives the 'structural visibility' (Freidson 1970:115) which is both a prerequisite for institutional legitimation and necessary for the protection of occupational boundaries (Kronus 1976:5).

Yet the peculiar nature of the British medical profession, sharply divided as it is even now between general practice and elite specialties, continued to prevent midwives from accomplishing their overall goal of *occupational power*. Denied hospital privileges by more powerful specialists, the longstanding rival of the midwife, the general practitioner, remained a sharp thorn in the side of the midwifery occupation until well into the early decades of the 20th century, not least because care of pregnant clients remained the cornerstone of family practice (Lewis 1980:140). Mediocre education in the area of maternity care nevertheless hindered general practitioners from gaining substantial ground vis-à-vis their better qualified midwifery competitors (Peterson 1978).

The establishment of the British National Health Service in 1948 helped to eliminate many of the economic barriers which had been responsible for the decades-long competition for clients between midwives and general practitioners, and both occupational groups gained a level of financial security hitherto unknown. Midwives were also provided the unique opportunity to embark upon a new career line—salaried government employment in the emerging maternity hospitals strategically located all over the country. These novel sites of midwifery practice—in many ways resembling the mothercare centres then taking shape in Sweden—awarded midwifery staff a degree of economic security, relative freedom from medical and administrative authority structures, and at the same time an avenue of escape from the often debilitating conditions of homebirth attendance.

Although still legal, domiciliary midwifery practice eventually became increasingly uncommon in Britain at the beginning of the post-WW II period. Clients, too, showed preference for the small maternity wards, which provided state-of-the-art midwifery care as well as speedy access to life-saving medical expertise and equipment in case of need. Labour and delivery in the small hospital setting had the further advantage of allowing expectant mothers to temporarily escape the discomforts of often overcrowded living quarters and heavy workloads—until their inevitable return to family life at the end of the postpartum period (Lewis 1980:132–4). A remodelled midwifery service also included strategically located regional medical centres for complicated deliveries, as well as a flying squad of ambulances which carried medical equipment and trained staff to distressed clients.

Not surprisingly, during this period there was little clamour for homebirth practice in Britain. Maternity units organised on the basis of a midwifery rather than medical model secured midwives relatively high occupational standing, access to a steady flow of clients, medical back-up and life-saving equipment, and the opportunity to upgrade their knowledge and bedside skills through frequent collegial interaction. Furthermore, an organisational schedule, a workplace separate from clients' homes, and a guaranteed salary allowed midwives to arrange their time and effort efficiently, without concern for inadequate transportation, poor working conditions or complications during abnormal labour and delivery.

In the past few decades, however, the British National Health Service has increasingly come under attack by conservative politicians. A rational efficiency model has been adopted by health authorities in order to trim the portion of the national budget allotted for health care spending. As a result, the hard-won autonomy only recently achieved by the midwifery occupation has come under threat. There is a growing fear among midwives that, though they still assist during the majority of deliveries, the expanding rationalisation of the National Health Service, which has led to the elimination of many small maternity units and the construction of large bureaucratic hospitals, will eventually result in a full-scale medicalisation of childbirth and medical dominance of midwifery. British midwives foresee a future in which they will find themselves on a par with the North American obstetrical nurse—"a mere minder of machines and hand-maiden to the obstetrician" (Donnison 1981:10).

The rising apprehension of British midwives is well-founded. Studies of maternity-care delivery in Britain indicate that large-scale organisational and technological changes have already significantly altered midwifery practice, fragmenting midwives' work while simultaneously blocking continuity of client care. As Walker (1972:88) observes:

> By becoming an employee of a large hospital, the midwife becomes part of an administrative hierarchy subjected to the fragmentation of work and division of labour found in other organisations.She tends to specialise in one aspect of maternity care whether it is the antenatal clinic, the delivery unit, or postnatal ward. The patients pass from one department to another in a system of progressive patient care which is sometimes alluded to by both mothers and midwives as a 'conveyer belt' system.

Major restructuring of childbirth arrangements in present-day Britain in the direction of greater bureaucratisation of midwives' work has resulted in the emergence of consumer health and midwifery movements calling for an adequately funded decentralised structure of maternity care, and even for a return of birth to the home (Oakley and Houd 1986:17–47).

Yet there remains a small circle of British health-care activists who, while sympathetic to calls for the demedicalisation of childbirth and the releasing of midwives from patriarchal medical control, nevertheless believe that a come-back of homebirth may not be desirable for either midwives or birthing clients. They instead lend support to a maternity arrangement comparable to the Swedish mothercare centre, where midwives in state-financed health centres take a primary role in the care of normal birthing women. Only pregnant women deemed at risk are referred to a general practitioner who, like the midwife, is a salaried employee rather than an independent contractor in the market (Walsh 1989). Although still a marginal segment of maternity-care services in Britain, this innovative system of birthing care in small government-funded midwifery-staffed health organisations, according to recent studies (Foster 1989), has led to considerable satisfaction on the part of both birthing women and midwives, who are able to organise childbirth relatively free from direct control by medical specialists and bureaucratic administrators.

THE UNITED STATES

Early developments in American midwifery to a large extent parallel British developments. This should come as no surprise considering that the first immigrants to the New England colonies carried with them many of the customs and traditions of the Mother Country. Originally, female lay healers attended colonial women during childbirth and often extended their care to the newborn and other household members in need of emergency aid (Wertz and Wertz 1977). Biographical sketches of a small number of colonial midwives are useful as historical evidence:

> One of the earliest midwives in the Massachusetts Bay Colony was Briget Lee Fuller, wife of Deacon Samuel Fuller. She travelled on the *Mayflower* and probably aided in the three births that occurred during the Atlantic crossing. She continued to serve as a midwife at Plymouth until her death in 1664. Epitaphs of various other women further attest to their value as midwives. The inscription on the tombstone of Ann Eliot, the wife of the Indian missionary, John Eliot, bears testimony to her services as a midwife. The epitaph of Elizabeth Phillips, whose death in 1761 brought an end to her more than forty-year career as a New England midwife, stated that she had "by ye blessing of God, ... brought into this world above three thousand children" (Litoff 1978:4).

By the 19th century, however, notable differences in maternity-care delivery had developed between Britain and the United States. In the U.S., where a democratic ideology discouraged state legislatures from passing statutory requirements for medical training (Starr 1982), where there existed no landed aristocracy and, equally important, where there emerged significant numbers of 'male midwives' (as obstetricians were initially called) without the protection of a counterpart to the British Royal College of Physicians and Surgeons to win for them an exclusive mandate over abnormal childbirth, the call to upgrade midwifery from lay to professional standing found little fertile ground (Arney 1982:39–40). On the contrary, access to the traditional lay midwife's homebirth clientele emerged as a high priority for the fledgling profession of obstetrics trying to gain a foothold in the childbirth market. These new medical specialists of 'women's diseases' fought vigorously to secure an ever firmer hold on the midwife's traditional domain of practice. Ultimately, they succeeded in placing most aspects of female reproduction under their own umbrella, to an extent unknown among their counterparts in other Western countries. The occupation of midwifery was in the U.S. increasingly discarded in favour of a 'single standard of obstetrics.' As Donnison (1981:8) comments:

> [P]rofessional uncertainty among American obstetricians led many to argue that as long as pregnancy and parturition were regarded as normal events, and the midwife in consequence was allowed to continue practising, their specialty would never receive the recognition they considered it deserved as an integral part of scientific medicine. Only the obstetrician, they argued, could give the American mother the obstetrical care she needed.

Despite the eventual victory of the profession of obstetrics over midwifery, as late as in 1910 approximately 50 percent of all births in New England were still attended by lay midwives in clients' homes (Kobrin 1966). But the vast majority of these midwives were poor immigrant women and black grannies who lacked the formal education credentials, organisational base, and aristocratic patronage of their British counterparts which might have helped them gain access to the political machinery then taking shape in industrial America (Donegan 1978; Litoff 1986).

At the same time, the emerging middle classes were increasingly alarmed by high maternal and infant mortality rates. Obstetricians were quick to point to the "hopelessly dirty, ignorant, and incompetent" midwives as the root cause (quoted in Kobrin 1966:351), although statistical data from the period clearly indicate that general practitioners and many obstetricians themselves were at least as negligent and unhygienic in their practices as the granny midwives (Wertz and Wertz 1979).

Obstetricians, nevertheless, continued their call for the elimination of the 'double standard' of maternity-care practice allegedly 'ruining the nation.' The result was a drawn-out midwifery debate between 1900 and 1920, during which both sides accused each other of incompetence and lack of genuine commitment to clients. Eventually the obstetricians won the day, not least because of strong backing from the powerful American Medical Association. Midwifery was frequently portrayed as an antiquated 'folk occupation' that had no place in modern America (Stevens 1971). In the words of J.L. Huntington, a prominent Boston obstetrician active in the dispute: "as soon as the immigrant is assimilated, ... then the midwife is no longer a factor in his home" (quoted in Kobrin 1966:257).

The centralisation of maternity care in large maternity hospitals that began in the 1920s granted U.S. obstetricians the stronghold they wanted, opening the door for the inclusion of pregnancy and childbirth — normal and abnormal alike — under the medical umbrella. Most U.S. states eventually modelled their maternity-care legislation after the Eastern pattern established in Boston and New York, bowed to the demands of the obstetrical profession, and banned midwifery altogether.

With rapid urban and industrial growth after World War II, U.S. midwifery increasingly became a marginal occupation. The average number of deliveries attended by midwives dropped significantly, while their overall birth attendance took a nosedive. It was clear that pregnant women, at least in the middle classes, were deserting the midwife. Modern American women no longer viewed maternity as an uncomplicated 'natural process' during which a lay attendant only needed to 'stand by,' letting nature take its course. Instead, there emerged an increasing demand for *obstetrical* care across metropolitan America. As Kobrin (1966:363) explains:

> [There was] a growing public demand from women, who were becoming increasingly self-conscious about their own welfare, and who were still infected with the reforming zeal of the Progressive Era which had lead to their enfranchisement ... With 'womanhood' no longer rooted in the domestic, 'natural' environment, or perhaps reflecting release from such roots, the 'natural' way of doing things was losing its appeal for the many emerging American women, and the obstetrician was increasingly there to reap the results of a growing anxiety about childbirth.

In summary, the occupation of midwifery took a remarkably different path in the United States than in most other Western countries. Although at first adopting a similar traditional lay pattern, American midwives were unable to combat the more powerful profession of obstetrics in order to gain the necessary popular support for inclusion of normal childbirth under a modern midwifery rather than medical umbrella.

Yet this is not the whole story. In isolated pockets of America, the traditional lay midwife was in fact eliminated only recently (Mongeau *et al.* 1961; Dougherty 1982). Moreover, a counterpart of the trained European midwife, the American nurse-midwife, although small in number, emerged in the early 1930s in order to serve those urban and rural poor without economic means to pay for medical care (Campbell 1946).

In 1925, an American graduate nurse and native of Kentucky, Mary Breckinridge, a midwife certified by the British Central Midwives' Board, established a nurse-midwifery program in the Kentucky Mountains. Breckinridge, joined in 1929 by other American midwives schooled in England and by immigrant midwives from the British Isles, formed the American Association of Nurse-Midwives [AANM]. State legislatures were pressured to provide a 'frontier nursing service,' and by 1934 the AANM had opened small maternity hospitals as well as established midwifery training programs in a number of southern (at that time, largely rural) states, including Georgia, North Carolina and Florida. Eventually, the AANM joined forces with counterparts at the urban-based Maternity Centre Association in New York City. Litoff (1978:126–27) writes that

> graduates of the MCA...went to Alabama, Maryland, and other southern states where they assisted in the training of 'grannies.' Furthermore, in 1941, the Maternity Centre Association sent some of its midwives to Tuskegee, Alabama, to help set up the Tuskagee Nurse-midwifery School. This school, which survived for six years, was established in order that black nurses from the South might be able to receive training in midwifery. Representatives from the MCA also participated in the establishment of a nurse-midwifery school in Santa Fe, New Mexico, in 1944.

Unlike her European counterpart, however, the emerging American nurse-midwife was no match for her competitor, the obstetrician, who enjoyed not only the authority of legal office but also a nation-wide medical monopoly over maternity-care delivery sanctioned by both state and federal legislatures (Starr 1982). Not until 1971, in fact, did the powerful College of Obstetricians and Gynecologists finally acquiesce to the nurse-midwives' role of primary attendant at childbirth.

Yet even today the majority of American nurse-midwives, especially in urban areas where the competition from obstetrics remains intense, practise as 'obstetrical nurses' expected to move to the side as soon as the obstetrician appears. Recent statistics gathered by the American College of Nurse-Midwives clearly demonstrate the present-day marginality of its members: 1,299 nurse-midwives practised in the U.S. between 1976–77, and of these only 548 were the senior birth attendant. They accounted for just one percent of deliveries in the United States (Anisef and Basson 1979:368–9). By

1985, the figure had risen to two percent, with 50 percent of their services going to the poor (Koch 1985).

The largely futile effort by American nurse-midwives to gain solid occupational turf results partly from the U.S. structure of maternity-care delivery. The United States stands alone among Western nations in promoting 'free-enterprise' health care (although Britain at present appears to be moving in a similar direction). The result has been a fragmentary health-care system that encourages huge profits for health corporations, provides sizable incomes for physicians, and leads to sharp inequality in care, largely depending upon clients' ability to pay for services rendered (Seward *et al.* 1984). These developments have been accompanied by the growth of ever larger health organisations or 'medical-industrial complexes' which have tended to reduce the scope of authority of many employees, including nurse-midwives (Ehrenreich and Ehrenreich 1978).

The American way of health-care delivery — 'corporate medicine' (Starr 1982) — not only leaves a large segment of its work force dissatisfied but is also comparatively costly in terms of human life. The U.S. spends more on health care services than most other developed nations, yet it has one of the highest infant mortality rates in the Western world (World Health Organisation 1981), a result which closely reflects sharp class and racial inequality in maternity-care services (Nelson 1986; Danziger 1986). It is likewise ironic that the country scores comparatively high on medical procedures such as episiotomies, inductions of labour, fetal monitoring, and forceps and Caesarian deliveries (Arms 1975). In fact, modern-day maternity care in most areas of the U.S. — based upon obstetrical dominance and bureaucratic organisation — is so oriented towards intervention that, as Haire (1972) points out, the birth experience is 'warped,' contorting it into an unnatural pathological event rather than an important physiological and emotional experience for the childbearing women. This situation of 'patriarchal/bureaucratic birth,' argues Shaw (1974), is in fact a form of 'forced labour.'

It is, therefore, hardly surprising that most of the writings on the 'male medical takeover of women's reproductive powers' are by American feminists. The intertwined lay midwifery/childbirth movements may be seen as concerted attempts by health activists to deepen public awareness of the 'theft of childbirth' (Rich 1975) — from both female midwives and pregnant women — by male doctors. Despite certain piecemeal reforms, such as the presence of fathers in the delivery room, prenatal classes for expectant parents, rooming-in of newborns with their mothers, and home-like birthing rooms in high-tech teaching hospitals, many feminists remain skeptical and speak about the 'cooptation' of their movement by a reformed medical profession. The more radical among them, like their British counterparts, have called for a full-scale return to independent midwifery in order to reinstate childbirth to its 'natural place,' the home, where pregnant women would again deliver their babies in partnership with the attending midwife (Rothman 1982; DeVries 1985). The outcome has been the establishment of a number of lay midwifery practices — some legal, others illegal — which now deliver a small percentage (fewer than five percent) of babies in clients' homes.

Nevertheless, some U.S. activists question the viability of homebirth for the majority of clients, especially poor pregnant women without adequate home conditions for giving birth or the ability to pay the attending midwife. They also point to the many problems of present-day homebirth practice — including pressure from the powerful medical and nursing establishments, constant client monitoring of their every action by the use of telephones, beepers and other mechanical communication devices and the threat of malpractice suits — which hamper professionalism in new ways. Given these less than ideal circumstances, a small number of U.S. health activists advocate instead a "middle-of-the-road" solution — free-standing birthing centres — financed by a national socialised health-care plan. A sprinkling of such small maternity organisations were opened in the early 1970s, many of which were federally funded through education heath grants (Leveen 1986). Preliminary research on the still existing birthing centres indicates that, by balancing the expectations of clients for a normal birth but also a safe delivery, birth centre midwives are indeed able to carry pregnant women through natural deliveries, thus granting them a dimension of occupational control over the reproductive process. At the same time, the health centre midwife, who typically is on salary, gains a measure of professional power from both consumers and obstetricians (Annandale 1987; 1988; Feldman & Hurst 1987; Sullivan & Weitz 1988). Nevertheless, among other things, the lack of secure funds, the growing pressure from local medical societies competing for ever dwindling numbers of paying birthing clients, and the escalation of midwifery as well as of medical malpractice insurance leave the future of the U.S. free-standing birth centres uncertain:

> Although FSBCs [Free Standing Birth Centers] serve fewer than one-half to 1 percent of American women annually..., they represent an important trend in obstetrical care — a trend toward the appropriate use of technology in childbirth and toward women and

their families having a voice in the medical management of the birth of their children. FSBCs are a rapidly growing alternative in the United States. Yet at the very time this alternative is solidifying, it is being threatened by the insurance industry crisis" (O'Reilly *et al.* 1986:207).

CANADA

Canada stands alone among Western nations in denying midwives — lay and formally trained alike — any legal status. This holds firm across provincial boundaries, with exceptions made only for a few peripheral areas, among them northern Newfoundland and Labrador, where medical practitioners are reluctant to take up long-term residency. Each Canadian province has a Medical Act, in most instances dating back to the 19th century, which grants the medical profession control over maternity-care delivery. Newfoundland and Labrador, which joined Canada only in 1949, is an exception to this Canadian trend. A Midwives' Act was established there in the 1920s (continually revised thereafter), which granted trained midwives control over normal childbirth. In fact, out of 210 countries recently surveyed, in addition to Canada, only eight developing countries — Venezuela, Panama, New Hebrides, Honduras, El Salvador, Dominican Republic, Columbia and Burundi — are without legislation allowing some form of midwifery practice (Phaff 1986).

This dismantling of Canadian midwifery has paradoxically occurred in conjunction with the establishment of a socialised health-care system that has often been praised for its comprehensive and universal programs. What explains this seemingly contradictory situation where pregnant women are deprived of a midwifery option but nevertheless enjoy maternity care free of charge? A brief examination of Canada's beginnings as a nation sheds some light upon this question.

Just like other former British colonies such as Australia (Willis 1983:92–124), the nascent Canadian state attempted throughout the late 19th and early 20th centuries to attract able-bodied workers from abroad to complement its small and scattered labour force.[1] Wave after wave of European immigrants sought refuge from the poverty and disease then rampant in their home countries, hoping to make a new beginning on the Canadian frontier. Many flocked to the industrial belt between present-day Toronto and Montreal where they faced unsanitary living conditions frequently worse than those they had left behind (Cosbie 1975).[2] Medical services, moreover, were poor and in many places nonexistent. The few 'learned physicians' in practice during the early industrial period largely catered to the small Canadian elite, and were known to treat all diseases with the same two remedies, opium and mercury (Cosbie 1975). Most immigrant families were forced to rely upon extended kin or their own healing cures to carry them through health crises, and parturient women called upon a local 'handy woman' to attend to their needs during the lying-in period (Buckley 1979).

Despite efforts by the fledgling Ontario medical profession to suppress traditional midwifery during the beginning stages of settlement, a shortage of trained physicians rendered such attempts futile. As one subscriber to the *Canadian Lancet* (4 [1873]:150) argued, without access to lay midwives, expectant mothers "who live in the back settlements... would be in a very distressing situation since the closest medical man was thirty or forty miles away." While the first Medical Act regulating the practices of 'physic and surgery' in Upper Canada in 1795 had made it illegal to practice midwifery without a licence, exempting only those with a university degree, the impracticality of such a ruling soon became apparent, and made the medical profession vulnerable to public criticism:

> How absurd, how cruel, how meddling that a poor woman in labour could not have assistance from a handy, sagacious neighbour being liable to be informed upon and fined (Canniff 1894:22).

Not surprisingly, this original Medical Act was repealed in 1806 and lay midwifery remained immune from the licensing laws of the Medical Board until the last decades of the 19th century. The repealed Act of 1806 provided

> that nothing in this Act contained shall extend... to prevent any female from practising midwifery in any part of the Province, or to require such [a] female to take out such a licence as aforesaid (Canniff 1894:30–2).

As the 19th century drew to a close, however, the traditional lay midwifery system, based in the home and in the still intact rural community, could not possibly meet the needs of large segments of the Canadian population living under unstable circumstances in the emerging urban environment. Poor and destitute pregnant women, without kinship or friendship networks to provide them with food and shelter during their confinement, fell outside the traditional homebirth arrangement. Some of these forsaken women were given physical aid by philanthropic institutions, such as the Society for the Relief of Women during their Confinement, established in 1820 in Ontario (Oppenheimer 1983). Yet such voluntary organisations did not provide accommodation, which left the few hospitals with the task of providing shelter to homeless parturient women. These original Ontario hospitals, moreover, infamous for their over-crowded, unsanitary conditions and abysmally poor medical treatment based upon questionable remedies such as bloodletting, purging and leeching, often did more harm than good, and were widely feared. As a contemporary observed about one Ontario hospital of the period:

> It is worthy of remark that most of the lower orders have such an aversion to the hospital, that they will not submit to be removed until they are conveyed hither in a state of insensibility (Cited in Oppenheimer 1983:40).

The traditional lay midwifery system was also powerless in combatting the high infant and maternal mortality rates accompanying early industrialisation in Canada. As late as the 1920s (when the first national statistics became available) the Canadian infant mortality rate was 92 per 1,000 live births and the maternal mortality rate was 5.6 maternal deaths per 1,000 birthing women (Buckley 1979:134–5). As one commentator pointed out at the time: "more babies die in Canada yearly, under one year old, from preventive causes than soldiers have been killed during the war" (Buckley 1979:133).

Social reformers searched for an effective way to halt the 'slaughter of the innocents.' Eventually maternity clinics and infant milk depots were opened and mothercare classes were established. Yet such worthwhile endeavors were mainly confined to the larger urban areas and did little to reduce the national infant and maternal mortality rates. Across the vast Canadian landscape—in the lumbering camps of the Pacific coast, the farming communities scattered throughout the Prairies, the industrial towns of Ontario and Quebec, and the fishing settlements in the Atlantic region— medical care was virtually unattainable, lay midwifery services were spread thin, and the new public health programmes beyond reach for the most needy.

A 'cottage hospital system,' modelled after developments in Scotland, was finally chosen on a trial basis in the province of Ontario in an attempt to ease the situation there. The plan was to establish a number of small hospitals in strategic locations, where local inhabitants would receive primary health care, including maternity services by salaried birth attendants. In one crucial respect the central Canadian version of the cottage hospital scheme was different, however—trained *nurses*[3] rather than midwives were to staff the emerging maternity wards. Unlike its British counterpart, the Canadian nursing occupation held a relatively powerful position in the health division of labour and it was able to prevent midwives from gaining a footing in the proposed cottage hospital system; nursing educators, supported by the medical profession, maintained that midwifery was an outdated occupation belonging to the 'dark ages' and unnecessary in an 'up-to-date' country such as Canada (Buckley 1979:144–5).

While successful in banning midwifery, the nursing profession nevertheless remained unable to fill vacant positions in the cottage hospitals. Nurses, attracted to urban life, were often not at all keen on employment in the small maternity hospitals located in areas where, as one temporary nurse sojourner complained "you would hear the coyotes howling around" (quoted in Buckley 1979:142). In fact, the incipient cottage hospital system never got off the ground: nursing recruits were reluctant to take positions outside of Ontario's metropolitan centres, and the comparatively well organised nursing occupation succeeded in blocking midwives from practising on the new maternity wards. According to Biggs (1984:117):

> Efforts to introduce a system of midwifery in Canada were cir-
> cumscribed by the professional interests of nurses who wished to
> retain their recently earned professional status and by physicians
> who wished to protect their financial interests as well as maintain
> their monopoly over childbirth.

By the late 1920s the present-day structure of the Canadian maternity-care system was all but in place. The midwife's modern substitute, the obstetrical nurse, was awarded the less than prestigious position of 'doctor's handmaiden' and expected to show "wifely obedience to the doctor, motherly self-devotion to the patient and a form of mistress/servant discipline to those below" (Buckley 1979:134). The medical profession's perspective on childbirth, as a potentially *abnormal* event needing continuous monitoring and frequent obstetrical intervention, surfaced as the dominant view endorsed by all care givers on the maternity ward, including the new obstetrical nurse. Provinces situated both west and east of Ontario and Quebec eventually followed the same modernisation path, suppressing midwifery and promoting the less autonomous obstetrical nursing specialty. The common view was expressed by a physician: "the art of midwifery belongs to prehistoric times; the science of obstetrics is the latest recognition of all ancient sciences" (quoted in Biggs 1983:32). The question of 'lady nurses or midwives' was ultimately decided in favour of the former, although they gained little by way of occupational autonomy in the process.

Such a maternity-care arrangement was not only detrimental to central Canadian midwifery. As Buckley (1979:149) notes, pregnant women, too, were disadvantaged:

> [I]n the short run, the lack of trained midwives resulted in the loss of life for many Canadian infants and mothers; in the long run the exclusion of trained midwives ensured that future generations of women would be denied an alternative to the gynecological and obstetrical monopoly held by the predominantly male profession.

The lack of attention to the needs of birthing clients and midwives alike continues to prevail even now throughout most of Canada. Although providing a comprehensive package of medical services, Canada falls short in the area of *primary health* care. In some ways adopting the rational efficiency model of present-day Britain and the United States, Canadian politicians have moved towards greater bureaucratisation of health-care services. This political change has been accompanied by heated public debate. Vocal midwives and some of their client supporters have called for a turn away from the medicalisation of maternity care and from the medical dominance of paraprofessional workers and for the reinstitution of *midwives* as the major care givers of birthing clients (Barrington 1985; Burtch 1988).

Canadian activists, just like their counterparts in present-day Britain and the United States, remain divided concerning the ideal setting of midwifery practice, however. Should they support a new version of the traditional fee-for-service system where lay midwives practised in clients' homes? Or should the route taken be fashioned after Sweden, where trained midwives care for normal maternity clients at local neighbourhood mothercare centres? At present the midwifery and maternity-care movements in Canada remain split on the issue: some Canadian health care activists favour a return to childbirth in the home, while others advocate a compromise solution—the free-standing health centre option—that is similar to the alternative now endorsed by reform groups in the United States and Britain. A recently launched experimental project which involves the operation of four government-funded free-standing birthing centres in the province of Ontario may provide valuable data in regard to the latter option.

SUMMARY

Comparison of the maternity-care arrangements in five Western countries reveals substantial heterogeneity of source of funding, place of birth and senior attendant across and even within national borders. Discontent among midwives and clients with existing services is in evidence in several of the countries discussed, yet the path forward remains largely uncertain.

Data on midwifery in present-day Sweden point to small health organisations as a viable alternative form of maternity care. Such organisations can balance clients' desire for safety with their psycho-social needs and at the same time allow midwives a measure of occupational power available neither in the home nor in the bureaucratic hospital environment. An analogous development in present-day Britain, the United States and Canada (although still in its early beginnings) – of free-standing government-funded birthing centres staffed by trained midwives – also points to progressive maternity-care reform even in those Western countries where medicalisation and deprofessionalisation are most advanced.

Findings on the transformation of midwifery in Newfoundland and Labrador contribute further evidence that midwives located in small health organisations – in this particular case, in cottage hospitals – can achieve a balance between the 'art' and the 'science' of their occupation. Chapter 3 draws extensively on interview and secondary data in an attempt to highlight some of the characteristic features of the work worlds of Newfoundland and Labrador midwives.

Balancing Community and Organisation: Midwives' Work Worlds

3

We were well-rounded midwives, used to coping with everything. The cottage hospital was a family-centered place; it was not clinical, not an alien atmosphere. Maternity care was flexible and without [doctor] interference. And there was seniority. You were in the job field for so long that general staff duties were just pie—nothing to it! But at the cottage hospital you could do supervisory work and still be with the women. It was the beauty of a small unit. In the larger unit, where you're running, you delegate so much of your role that the patient is limited to 'how are you today, Mrs. Brown?'
Cottage Hospital Midwife

The view of this respondent is not exceptional. All midwives interviewed in my Newfoundland and Labrador sample distance themselves from the reconstruction of independent midwifery found in recent writings on their occupation. At the same time, they are quick to point out that in many ways midwives' work in present-day large bureaucratic hospitals has become medicalised and deprofessionalised. They are forced to perform below their expertise and to practice under conditions that render them mere 'handmaidens' of doctors and administrators.

Both retired and active midwives, many with a background of early work experience in clients' homes and rural health units (in some cases also in small and large hospital sites), conclude that only the modest cottage hospitals that flourished between the 1930s and 1960s gave midwives a measure of professionalism not enjoyed by their counterparts in traditional homebirth attendance, isolated clinic practice, or current bureaucratic employment. A variety of factors enhance midwives' occupational status: adequate remuneration; independence from direct community and family control; liberty to pursue maternity care as a specialty; balanced access to clients, colleagues, technology and medical back-up; availability of a pleasant, adequately equipped work environment; arrangement of a formal schedule with sufficient off-work time for personal development; and finally, avenues of career mobility. This chapter traces midwives' differential achievement of these crucial attributes of professionalism by examining, in historical sequence, their four major sites of practice—traditional homebirth attendance, rural clinic work, cottage hospital practice, bureaucratic employment.

TRADITIONAL HOMEBIRTH ATTENDANCE

Professionalism is intimately tied to the capacity of making a living from services rendered. Viewed from this perspective, the work of the traditional lay midwife cannot be classified as a full-time occupation, since it did not provide her with an opportunity for reliable remuneration. Granny midwives did not enter into a formal social contract with local clients. Community notions of the midwifery role—to serve the rich and poor alike, to never refuse a client—overruled the calculation of reward for services rendered.

It would be shortsighted to assume that midwifery was atypical in this regard. On the contrary, other service occupations found themselves in a comparable situation under premodern conditions of practice. The origins of health visiting in Britain, for example, parallel the beginnings of midwifery in Newfoundland and Labrador:

> There is a sense in which health visitors have always existed. Every community has some members who act as sources of knowledge or advice on particular topics. Thus, those who have successfully raised families or avoided serious illness may share the supposed secrets of their success. While this task may be carried out for marginal gain, the rewards may be primarily symbolic in the status and deference which accrue to them from the recognition of their superior expertise. Part of this task may include home visiting within a pattern of kinship, neighbourhood or feudal obligations (Dingwall 1983:605–6).

Nor was the economic precariousness of the granny midwife's role unique among inhabitants of her Newfoundland and Labrador village. It was shared by most adults, who often subsisted by bartering with local merchants, exchanging their hard-earned catch of the sea and produce of the land for winter supplies (Benoit 1990). This left the average household with little cash to pay the midwife. If compensated at all, midwives were often paid in local currency— typically vegetables, animal products or local craft. One granny midwife explains how the barter system worked:

> Some women would give $5 or $10 and that was for the whole 10
> days. When they didn't give me money, they'd give vegetables and
> things like that. It was all money in a way, my dear. But I've done
> it for a lot of people who didn't have nothing. And others, if they
> couldn't give it to me at the time, then maybe later they'd give me
> a cabbage—you know, things like that. Most of them tried their best
> but some of them were pretty bad off them days.

As long as the barter system persisted, the granny midwife had
little control over the remunerative value of her work, providing
community aid and special care to pregnant women without as-
surance of immediate reward. Exchange was generalised: an
unwritten agreement between the granny midwife and the locals
stipulated that at some future time the client, or one of her kin,
would pay what was due, in money or in kind. The granny woman's
services were in a way like gifts or tokens of appreciation.[1] There
was no fixed price attached to them; they were given in a context of
mutual trust within a system of generalised reciprocity.

This early barter system virtually eliminated economic exploitation of clients by would-be granny entrepreneurs. Traditional lay
midwives belonged to those preliterate occupations in which it is the
clients who determine their own needs as well as the mode of
payment for services rendered, in contrast to modern professionals
who "do not merely serve, [but who] define the very wants they serve"
(Hughes 1971:424). Granny midwives, poor themselves, and dependent upon an impoverished clientele, were hardly able to practise
the type of professional dominance or widespread social control
which some feminists and other social critics maintain is typical of
contemporary elite professions, particularly medicine.[2] They
gathered a clientele through recommendations from satisfied cus-
tomers, attending needy pregnant women at their own behest,
without expectation of considerable economic reward. This helped
to give local clients access to midwifery services, without serious
worry about cost and repayment. Granny midwives had to abide by
the unwritten community code that in emergency situations of any
kind a call for help was not to be refused, whether it could be
remunerated or not.

The traditional lay midwife's actual reward, in kind or in money,
also depended upon the general economic situation of local families,
which was determined by fluctuations in international (especially
fish) markets as well as by geographic and weather conditions.
Significant improvements in living standards occurred in the aftermath of the 1929 global economic crisis (referred to by granny

midwives as the 'Dirty Thirties') and especially in the post-Confederation era (after 1949). Yet even in the 1950s midwives could not count on earning a living by their work. One granny woman describes her own situation:

> I got $5 when I started out—for nine days, going back and forth. And then somebody rose it to $10 and I'd do the same for that. And then somebody rose it to $20, so the last of it I got $20. But sometimes I didn't get paid, didn't get paid yet. Well, [if a woman didn't have cash], I'd just tend her, just like the rest. I didn't refuse them. No, couldn't do that. I had to do the best I could for everyone. If a woman come down now, I would do the same thing for her that I done then.

Another granny describes one of her peers:

> She was a poor old granny, a very poor woman. She had a very big family. Her husband would come home and wouldn't move. He'd sit around and wouldn't go outside the house. She made a living like that. She charged $5 but some people couldn't afford even that. I used to give her my old clothes. She was pretty poor, the poor thing.

Precarious economic circumstances were not the only block to occupational autonomy. In the organisation of her daily practice, too, the granny midwife lacked discretion. Like many other premodern craft workers, granny midwives can be described as 'peripatetic entrepreneurs' (Sussman 1982:44–50), sometimes travelling considerable distances to clients' homes since catchment areas might have encompassed a radius of 30 miles or more. The main means of transportation were horsecart in summer and dog sled in winter. Once roads were built and automobiles arrived, mobility became somewhat easier, and the telephone, even if there typically was only one in each community, helped to reduce the number of home visits, postponing others to a more convenient time. But many isolated communities remained without these modern amenities until well into the post-World War II period. One midwife recalls her travels to clients' homes:

> I had to walk everywhere. At that time there was no phone. Somebody would come for me. They would have to walk up and I would have to walk back. Well, I remember the Harbour Road was three miles long and I walked it once in 35 minutes! I was a pretty good walker—except in winter, when we'd use a horse. The husband or some relative would come. But I never used a clinic or anything like that, just house visiting.

Commuting irregular distances in every type of weather was only one of the unattractive conditions accompanying homebirth practice. Without a separate workplace in which to carry out prenatal check-ups and conduct deliveries, the traditional lay midwife was expected to adapt her activities to the often desperate home conditions of clients. Although the birthing chamber was supposed to be stocked with fresh linen, cleaning materials and baby clothes, the granny midwife frequently arrived at the labour scene after a long journey only to find her client ill-prepared, with a crowd of children hovering around her as well. Such circumstances soon taught the homebirth attendant to carry a 'personal suitcase' (midwifery bag) containing essential supplies in anticipation of inadequate equipment. As one of them comments:

> There was some that was well off and some that was poor off. I wouldn't like to explain all that I saw. A lot of things wouldn't be nice to say, you see. A lot of things was not there. Perhaps no sheets. One woman on an old coat. They mightn't have nothing to put under them, maid. I'd have to tear up something. I always carried stuff with me. I had to, 'cause perhaps they didn't have anything when I'd get there. I had to have something to work with. They might not have even blankets and diapers for the baby. But she was there in the bed, laid there, and I had to get on with it.

The traditional lay midwife's control over her working conditions was circumscribed in other respects as well. Homebirth attendance demanded task-orientation and extreme flexibility, the necessity of being on call around-the-clock, whatever her own family situation. Often there were several deliveries at once ("it never rained but it poured"), resulting in an extremely demanding work pace, with little time for personal life. As one granny midwife recalls:

> My man was away at the trap line or fishing most of the time and so when he be out I'd have to leave my own young ones alone. I had to go just the same. I didn't mind the work, but I couldn't be gone all the time and handle the rest at home. But they'd always send for me and they really thought that I had to go and yet I'd feel my responsibility for my family. But if there was any way I could help them I should and I did. Some of them, after they'd send for me, I just be in through the door and they'd be delivering their child. And then I'd go home once a day—I had a husband and kids, hey—'til the 10 days was up. I was just skin and bones. Worked all day and night.

Of course, some granny midwives were able to rely on the help of their husbands or, especially if they lived in villages, to arrange for a relative or neighbour to temporarily take over their household duties. As one granny notes: "My husband would be home usually. And if not, I'd get someone to come in. You know, at that time there was seven families living in the area. So we'd always call on each other if we needed help with anything. Everyone helped." Childcare services freely offered by local inhabitants did little to ease other stressful aspects of traditional lay midwifery, however. The granny midwife's work was in a very real sense never done. She had to face the unknown in all kinds of weather, even when ill or tired or when her own children were bedridden. She never had vacations or work leaves; her work schedule was all-consuming, inescapable. Lack of sleep was inevitable:

> I would stay with the new mother three or four nights, you know; sometimes even longer. I'd get a break maybe in the night after I put the baby with the mother. I used to be glad to get home and get a good sleep. Yes, I remember I'd always try to have a good sleep when I got home.

Although some grannies had more stamina than others for coping with unpredictable time schedules, even stalwart midwives often broke under the strain. One of them describes how her heavy case load jeopardised her health:

> I used to break a lot of rest. One time I was three weeks attending deliveries, never stopped. I went to one woman and I was only there four hours before I had to go to another one. I'd just get my clothes off and get in bed and a knock come on the door: 'I wants you to come with me. My wife is sick.' I'd get up there and put on me clothes and go on. Every week like that. Perhaps sometimes twice a week. [In the end] it was getting too much for me. I was really beaten out.

And pregnancy leaves were unknown. The outcome was sometimes unfortunate:

> I used to walk to my maternity cases. I remember one time when I was pregnant myself and I went to one woman. I delivered her. I came out and I fell into the ice! I went down to [my chest], and of course I was scared for myself. I had twins but they only lived four days and I blamed that for it. They were lovely but they were born before they should—premature—just panting they were. But it couldn't be helped, I suppose.

Nor did the traditional lay midwife have access to other service workers to help meet the needs of her widely dispersed clientele. While a few 'jobbed around' with a travelling doctor or trained nurse at the onset of their careers, and some were periodically helped by apprentices or neighbours, most worked alone. Personal contact with colleagues in neighbouring communities was rare, preventing even occasional allocation of work tasks, exchange of knowledge and the emergence of an informal work culture. Instead, as one midwife relates, granny women were forced by circumstance to "get on with it alone 'cause someone had to help the mothers and there was no one else to do it, you know."

It should also be noted that not only were the duties of the traditional lay midwife performed without access to a circumscribed division of labour; they were, in addition, both time-consuming and onerous, going far beyond present-day notions of midwifery as predominantly concerning reproductive care. One granny midwife describes some of the labour-intensive tasks required during the lying-in period:

> When the woman would go into labour, someone would come and fetch me. I would born the baby and tell her what to do. I generally called in another woman—the mother or a neighbour—with me, you know, to take care of the baby 'till I get the woman done but often there was no one with me. All alone. I'd cook meals, clean the clothes, things like that. Then I would visit her everyday 'til the 10 days was up.

Moreover, professional nursing and medical help was so rarely available at the village level that, as one granny midwife starkly states: "we could be sick and die and be buried and they [the travelling nurse and doctor] wouldn't know. That's how often we saw them!" Rural birthing clients were forced to fall back on the limited knowledge of local lay healers. One of them relates her own experience:

> The doctor and nurse weren't really into it then, unless it was a difficult one. You had to be pretty sick, too. When I had my first one I took sick. Three days on my knees. Gosh, I almost died. We sent someone for the doctor and he told them: 'if she's not dead in the morning, I'll be down.' He never come but I got through.

The lack of access to adequate birthing technology confounded the situation, and as a result clients suffered, often seriously. A granny describes one of her own painful deliveries:

> The midwife was in the bedroom and my child was being delivered but, oh, I had a hard time. I tore open three inches and then the head came and the midwife had nothing to deaden that. She put stitches in live! See, we never had nothing for that then. They used to use 'tackle,' the stuff for sewing boots or shoes, or anything like that.

Another granny also remembers personal troubles during childbirth. Luckily, her village was in reach of a recently opened cottage hospital:

> I didn't have any trouble having them but I used to always sort of bleed afterwards. The midwife didn't know why. She used to have to ship me to the hospital. Yes, I used to lose a lot of blood, and after my second one I had a breast infection on top of it!

Most traditional lay midwives, without such hospital access, were forced to face obstetrical crises with nothing more than a midwifery bag consisting of scissors, sterile towels, and a 'baby bundle' which included gauze and a string for tying the umbilical cord. Yet birth outcomes, although often painful, were usually successful. Many maternity situations now defined as problems requiring medication were considered normal events, best handled within the home environment. In particular, pains accompanying labour were believed to be 'God-given' and 'natural,' and new mothers were expected to bear with them. Most local clients, according to granny midwives, eventually learned to do just that, 'never making a fuss,' 'not knowing what it was like to be sick,' and becoming 'strong women' in the process. But some, especially younger, first-time mothers were more difficult cases. A granny midwife describes one kind of client whose suffering she failed to alleviate:

> Some of those having first babies were just scared to death. When they would have a pain, some would just screech and not do anything about it, you know. And when the pain was gone they would try and force the baby out. All I would tell them was the best way to push the baby out was to work with the pain. It took a lot of coaching sometimes, and a lot of patience.

Some women found the passage through childbirth extremely painful no matter how many times they had given birth. A granny tells of their plight:

> The women came and sometimes they would ask, 'why do we have to have such hard pain?' I'd sing a hymn or tell them something about what the Bible said, and that, even if they don't feel well, there was someone by their side anyway. They's was all hard workers and they were brought up hard. But sometimes it was a lot to bear.

Compared to present-day figures, however, infant mortality rates during the premodern era remained relatively high,[3] and the granny midwife was frequently required to perform the difficult task of comforting bereaving families. One granny invokes memories of infant deaths that she was powerless to prevent:

> When I looked after one woman, I didn't lose the baby right away
> when it was born but she was very small. Lived a few days and died.
> There was nothing we could do back then. And another woman lost
> one when I was with her. The doctor was hard to come by. I also
> remember when my sister-in-law was in childbirth. It was a long
> labour and it was winter time and there was lots of snow down. It
> took a long time to get up there, you know, and the baby died. I
> don't know really what the trouble was.

Another recounts the death of one twin:

> I lost one from a set of twins. He was breach and I just couldn't get
> him out. The mother had the flu, the cold, and she couldn't do
> much. So we lost the boy. His head was in there too long, I think.
> She was sad but she knew I did my best.

Virtually no family was able to boast the survival of all their
children, and although maternal deaths were less common, grannies had to console more than one husband left widowed in his prime
and forced to raise small children alone or, more typically, to divide
his offspring among relatives and neighbours willing to take in a
child.

In addition to their virtual helplessness in the face of obstetrical
abnormalities, traditional lay midwives had no way of providing safe
and effective birth control or abortion to their clients. While some
granny women prescribed local herbs (of doubtful effectiveness) to
ward off pregnancy, and advised new mothers to breastfeed their
infants on demand to help delay conception,[4] the majority of births
were unplanned and large families were the norm. A sympathetic
granny woman could merely console clients facing unwanted pregnancies by remarking that 'nobody likes to have so many babies.'
Not all traditional birth attendants were so comforting, however;
many held firmly to the belief that birth control "is the most foolish
thing that ever walked on the face of the earth." Another observes:

> I think its [birth control] awful for married people. It's up to Christ,
> how many children you have. If you're 'lotted a big family, that's all
> you can do with it. I'm glad there was nothing like that around then.
> You married. You had children. Whatever the Lord gave us, we had
> to bear.

Lack of safe and effective birth control was even more problematic for the granny midwife's unmarried clientele trying to cope
with traditional Christian standards of a woman's proper role.
Carrying this group of pregnant women, locally known as 'the fallen
ones,' through their reproductive passages often left the midwife

torn between conflicting impulses: to affirm community standards or to render sympathetic understanding to her stigmatised clients. One granny woman recollects the situation of non-wed mothers in her natal village:

> There weren't so many young girls pregnant then but, oh God, the ones that did! Us girls wasn't allowed to go and see a girl like that. Even if she was our friend, we wasn't allowed to go and see her. Sometimes we'd steal our way into their house, but if our parents found out, Lord, we'd be put out: 'no, you're not to be with a crowd like that!' Then there wasn't many men would accept their child and want to marry them. The girl would be left with nobody, except her child. Mothers mostly had to take them in and make them help do the housework and the washing. Some did marry after but [the husband] might not accept the child as his own and there would be a big fight and they might separate. I pitied them girls.

Even married birthing clients sometimes desperately needed the granny midwife's protection against insensitive members of their own household during the lying-in period. Without a separate workplace, however, both midwife and client felt 'under the thumb' of oppressive male kin. Traditional lay midwifery was no match for traditional *patriarchy*, as one granny woman clearly states:

> Some of the men was real rough on their women folk. Some was good providers but some was not so good. The woman belonged to him and no one else and nobody could come between. Once I was going to send for the doctor, but the husband wouldn't go for him. Ah, he was hard on his woman. She was more times drove out than she was in the house! There was a lot like him, some [even] beating up their women when they was pregnant. It would happen when the fella' be drunk. It was no easy job tending to women stuck with men like that!

One final observation should be made regarding the traditional lay midwife's situation. Apart from her maternity work, she was typically required to nurse the sick—farm animals as well as local inhabitants. She was a 'jill-of-all-trades.' Not only were these extra curing activities, like homebirth attendance, poorly paid, but they consumed a large portion of the granny midwife's already overtaxed time. While some accepted these general nursing and veterinary tasks without hesitation, others would have preferred to specialise, restricting their duties to genuine maternity work. The virtual absence of even rudimentary medical care, however, left local populations almost entirely dependent upon their own resources and on the local midwife's practical skills. As one granny woman reports:

I had to do the other things besides bringing along babies 'cause there was no nurse there for a long time. So I had to do that work too. When anybody got sick, they'd call. Colds and all those things. I done a lot for sick people [but] in the tail end of it I was getting a bit tired of it.

It is hardly surprising that many granny midwives eventually 'lost their nerve' and 'burnt out.' And it is telling that *none of those interviewed recommend a return to homebirth practice*. While noting the benefits for clients of personalised care in the home, all maintained that the 'cottage hospital was best': there the midwife enjoyed the freedom to choose maternity care as her special line of work; she had access to adequate supplies, a steady flow of clients and life-saving equipment; she was able to improve her esoteric knowledge and bedside skills through daily collegial interactions; and her separate workplace, formal schedule and guaranteed salary allowed her to organise her time and efforts efficiently, without worry about remuneration for services rendered or inordinate interference from kin and neighbours.

RURAL CLINIC WORK

The generation of Newfoundland and Labrador midwives that practised in the 1920s and early 1930s differed from traditional homebirth attendants in at least one crucial respect—regarding economic remuneration. Government funds were allocated to help pay the salaries of vocationally-trained midwives hired to initially supplement and eventually replace the aging granny women. This new employment opportunity freed midwives from economic dependency upon local clients. The freedom was only partial, however, since at least in those outport communities that were part of the Newfoundland Outport Nursing and Industrial Association (NONIA) scheme, local males were expected to contribute free labour for the construction of the clinic itself and local females were expected to contribute handicraft products to pay for its upkeep as well as contribute to the midwife's salary. Employee status did not result in much greater professionalism for midwives. As with the granny women, *site of practice* remained significant for the new midwives practising in the small rural clinics.

The first employed midwives consisted of two groups: a small number of recruits from Newfoundland and Labrador who had travelled abroad to attain midwifery credentials, and a majority of immigrant British midwives. Sometimes referred to by local clients as 'come-from-aways' (CFAs), the immigrants were to make up for the shortage of trained indigenous practitioners. In embarking upon

Gravestone of "granny midwife," Nora Ellsworth. The verse reads:

> An Angel of mercy to all who were ill,
> What love and devotion no verses can e'er tell.
> From early till late she was never behind.
> She poured out her life for the work of mankind.
> This tablet we raise with the wish and the prayer,
> That we'll meet her again where there's no pain nor tear.

Photo: Larry Harvey. Courtesy of Memorial University Folklore and Language Archives.

a program to import skilled midwifery labour, the government of the time hoped to entice the new 'guest workers' to take up permanent residency, oversee the development of formal education for local recruits, establish ethical guidelines and standards of midwifery practice, and professionalise the occupation. Despite significant achievements in this direction, prestigious posts for midwives were few. Prior to the mid-1930s, in fact, the typical career path led to appointment in hinterland clinics and nursing stations.

In contrast to their lay predecessors who typically practised in their natal community, the new generation of nurse-midwives, islander as well as immigrant, was part of an emerging secularised division of labour that involved a break from their *milieu natal* and mobilisation for practice in isolated areas usually at some distance from their own birthplace. These itinerant midwives were largely 'strangers' (Simmel [1908] 1971:143–9) among a domestic population which might include Indian, Inuit or French inhabitants, in addition to those of British ancestry. The tastes, outlook and values of the rural folk under their care often appeared foreign to them, sometimes even barbaric. All experienced initial culture shock. One early British midwife, recruited to a small community on the Labrador coast, recalls an episode from her own acculturation:

> I think the woman had only contractions when I got my first call to a homebirth. She was just sort of sitting there. So I said: 'Well, where do you want to be? Do you want to be on the bed?' Well, no, she wanted to be on the *floor*—to press against, you see... Meanwhile, the local granny midwife was supervising, although I ended up delivering the baby. Everything I did was all commented upon. I didn't know enough of the language to pick it up but I did a quick watch around. You don't give the baby to the mother. You give it to the oldest, the person with the most status. I said to myself: she looks like the oldest. 'Here, want the baby?' That was all approved of. After that I got called for just about all deliveries.

While a small number of these migratory midwives settled into the local community, eventually gaining the admiration and some-times even deference of clients willing to desert the granny midwives for the new 'trained ladies,' the majority remained temporary guests. Most, of course, had arrived in the expectation of leaving after a short stint of clinic work, but even those midwives intent upon longterm residency soon changed their minds. Despite the rewarding aspects of midwifery practice in isolated areas, professionalism remained an elusive promise. Indeed, in many ways the general frustrations experienced by both native-born and immigrant midwives in the outport clinics closely paralleled those of the granny women.

Originally, the clinic midwife lived above her workplace. Separation of home and office was virtually impossible, leaving her at the mercy of local inhabitants and with little control over her timetable or pace of work. The midwife had to attend distressed clients who arrived at the clinic door at inconvenient times. Moreover, although she might draw up a formal office schedule, local inhabitants continued to expect house calls both day and night. Clinic midwives were forced to spend many hours travelling across land and sea to attend bedridden patients and birthing clients in their homes, where conditions were at times as desperate as those faced by their granny forerunners. As one clinic midwife describes her hectic work schedule:

> When you were at the nursing station, you were *living* there. Clinic was downstairs and the living room was on the same floor as the ward. You were in it! You didn't know anybody and there wasn't time to go out at all. How many jobs are there where you spend all your time helping on your time off?

Most nursing stations and rural clinics were rudimentary physical plants. Although later enlarged and provided with emergency medical supplies, many conveniences taken for granted in hospital settings, including a separate maternity ward and basic obstetrical supplies, remained unavailable. Isolation in a peripheral setting also meant operating outside a formal division of labour, with no immediate access to medical specialists during abnormalities and, depending upon budgetary constraints, perhaps not even a 'local hand' to deal with the manual chores involved in running a tiny yet exceptionally busy work site. Furthermore, without a secretary, the clinic's records and accounts had to be managed by the midwife herself. And like the granny woman's jill-of-all-trades role, rural clinic practice imposed the responsibilities of a general practitioner, which often conflicted with maternity duties. The clinic midwife was not merely the only health consultant in the community; she was the administrator of the infirmary, the local veterinarian, and sometimes the social worker or even policewoman: numerous informal job assignments were brought together into one generalised service role, with midwifery squeezed in between all these others. One clinic midwife describes the difficult working circumstances that eventually led to her resignation:

> I was the only midwife there. In the summer you did your home visiting by boat. There weren't any scheduled planes—you had to charter one. The nursing station was 'modern' in as much as you had an oil stove and hauled water connected to a pump. There was one telephone for the whole community. I had a crib and a couple

of baskets and two beds: one for the patient and one for myself! I had some drugs. In those days you had to have a good reason to send a woman out to hospital. And they didn't want to go 'cause they'd have to go early, leave their families, and the people [in the hospital] didn't speak their language. But some of those women wouldn't have survived. They really bled. It was scary. They placed too much trust in you. If you could get babies past their first birthday it was a relief!

Not all clinic midwives worked alone, however. In a small number of two-person health units, a primary care nurse was on hand to help ease the burden of responsibility, allowing the midwife precious moments of free time from her demanding work schedule and an opportunity to take much-needed and typically long-delayed holidays away from the community. Yet due to the perpetual shortage of both trained midwives and nurses to fill such positions, the promised partnership frequently remained just that, leaving the clinic midwife with a double work load to manage on her own. Even when a primary care nurse was recruited, the clinic midwife soon realised that working with a partner who lacked specialised maternity care knowledge and delivery experience had serious drawbacks, especially during obstetrical emergencies. The ultimate result, as one respondent relates concerning a colleague, was that "the poor girl was on call practically all the time anyway 'cause things did go wrong." Many midwives who did stints in nursing stations and rural clinics—with or without a nursing associate—observe that their premature grey hairs were the result of having to juggle so many countervailing demands.

Finally, isolation in a small-scale work setting without access to kin, acquaintances and like-minded colleagues, and with little free time to form new relationships, was difficult to bear in the long-term. Especially during the seemingly never-ending winter months, the clinic midwife easily felt trapped in an alien environment without basic consumer items (fresh foods, reading materials, theatre), opportunity for colleagueship or social life. In the words of one former clinic midwife:

It was the isolation of working above your level of competency and all that comes with loneliness, such as being able to share with peers what to do. You felt left out. Indeed, you could really feel that way when you were alone, no plane was coming, you had no mail for quite a few days, and you were on your last fresh apple. You felt that the other world was having a good time of it.

In brief, although their work situation was superior to that of the granny women in regard to economic security, the first generation of trained midwives recruited for work in rural clinics and nursing stations faced numerous difficulties, eventually leading to overall dissatisfaction with their peripheral location in the modernising maternity-care system. While a small number were able to ameliorate some of their problems by marrying into the community and, in a few cases, becoming seasoned part-time midwives, the vast majority experienced burnout after a few years of arduous clinic work. This was the case for native-born as well as immigrant midwives; neither were willing to sacrifice career and personal development indefinitely, despite the high community status sometimes awarded to them by local inhabitants. Some clinic midwives subsequently returned to their hometowns in Britain, perhaps finding employment in maternity hospitals there. Others, keen on making another go at it in Newfoundland and Labrador, sought work in the emerging cottage hospitals.

COTTAGE HOSPITAL PRACTICE

Compared to the isolated locales of the traditional grannies and the first generation of trained midwives — the home and rural clinic — the cottage hospital emerged as an ideal work environment, continuing the personalised client care of the old system based on home and secluded community while making available improved health facilities in an intimate, non-threatening hospital environment. The cottage hospitals were situated in developing towns with relatively stable economies and some access to consumer goods and modern facilities, allowing staff midwives to escape the debilitating consequences of rural isolation experienced by both their granny and clinic forerunners. Yet the cottage hospitals (most of which were 30-50 bed institutions employing five to 10 midwives on their modest maternity wards) never became large enough to generate the tight medical and managerial authority structures characteristic of the large high-tech hospitals of today. The result was a measure of genuine professionalism for cottage hospital midwives accessible neither to their earlier counterparts in home and clinic settings nor, as described below, to their later ones in larger, more bureaucratised sites of practice.

The professional freedom of cottage hospital midwives was multifaceted. To a greater extent than their predecessors, they specialised as full-fledged maternity attendants, calling on the staff physician only in cases of anticipated abnormality. According to my respondents, few local women were reluctant to forsake their homes for the comfort and safety offered by the cottage hospitals. One hospital midwife describes some of the advantages welcomed by her clients:

The women really got good care in the cottage hospital. It was unreal, the care they got there. If there wasn't any complications, they had a midwife and you really got to know them 'cause we stayed working at the hospital for a while. So we got to know the women personally, a close relationship. We sat with them and held their hands all the way through it. They felt relaxed and at home with us. We had time for them. They didn't mind a man doctor but I think they preferred us; they were more comfortable with women. I believe they really liked the old cottage hospital style. A small place, with warmth.

The first cottage hospitals were rather humble institutions administered by a skeleton midwifery and nursing team, a maintenance department comprising merely a janitor, maid and cook, and a medical staff consisting usually of a single doctor who spent as much time on the road as in the cottage hospital. Eventually higher salaries and more attractive work schedules were negotiated between cottage hospital midwives and health authorities. The physical plants were remodelled and support staff expanded, granting midwives greater freedom from the clean-up jobs and duty on neighbouring wards which, in the earliest days of the system, was expected of them. The medical personnel of the cottage hospitals were gradually augmented, making at least one physician available in case of obstetrical complication and releasing midwives from undertaking surgical procedures for which they had no specialised training.

By the early 1950s, most families outside the two cities in the province—that is, 60 per cent of the population—were served by the cottage hospitals, free of charge. Originally, the cottage hospital system required families with resources to pay an annual subscription fee of $10 ($5 for single persons), as well as an additional $10 fee per delivery. In 1958, however, this economic barrier was removed with the establishment of a new federal-provincial hospital insurance plan covering the costs of maternity and other health care services for all classes of clients within the cottage hospital catchment areas (Miller 1962).

By this time, homebirth attendance by granny women and clinic midwives had all but run its course, except in the most peripheral communities not connected by road. The result was that the bulk of rural and town women were giving birth in these small organisations, creating a sizable clientele for the increased midwifery staff. Yet such improvements did not lead to an erosion of the extended work mandates of cottage hospital midwives; rather, medical personnel remained remote from normal pregnancy and childbirth.

These unique conditions of practice—enhanced facilities without inter-professional rivalry—allowed staff midwives to specialise in maternity work to their own liking. They typically ran weekly perinatal clinics, carried each client through her labour and delivery, and often cared for the new mother and infant into the postpartum period, making home visits whenever required.

Cottage hospital midwives never became narrow specialists. Although their refashioned workplaces contained a separate maternity ward, all women expecting normal deliveries were roomed together. The present-day tendency towards fragmenting reproduction into distinct operations according to medical time frames was foreign to cottage hospital midwives. Instead, they viewed the stages of pregnancy and childbirth as interconnected, even inseparable. The design of the maternity ward closely reflected this midwifery model, essentially consisting of one large area, curtained off to afford some privacy to clients, but not structurally divided into individual wards. Cottage hospital midwives had the rare opportunity to utilise specialised maternity-care knowledge while working with all facets of the reproductive process. One of them describes how a noncompartmentalised environment also enhanced rapport between attendant and client:

> Coming to the cottage hospital to have a baby was like nothing, really. They came in, had their baby, and you'd try to give it to the mother right away to feed, just to stimulate sucking. You didn't take the baby away to a so-called nursery. The baby was no distance from the mother; she could hear it cry. It was just because the cottage hospital was so small. The mothers stayed three days or so and then packed and went home with their little ones in tow. We looked out to them in the community for 14 days after that.

While cottage hospital midwives practised in a 'controlled environment,' their workplace never developed the kind of tightly-woven structure characteristic of modern-day bureaucratic health organisations. Labour and delivery were scheduled events, but they remained open to negotiation between midwife and client, with the goal of accommodating the reproductive cycles of pregnant women, the work shifts of the midwifery staff and, inevitably, the unpredictable weather conditions. According to my informants, the practice of 'daylight obstetrics,' of booking clients prior to their natural due dates for early induction, that is often carried out today for the convenience of attending physicians (Heitlinger 1987; Eakins 1986), was unknown during this period.

Equally important, in contrast to homebirth attendance and rural clinic work, the cottage hospital granted some protection from family and community controls. Cottage hospital midwives could to some extent avoid the 24-hour call experienced by traditional lay midwives and their counterparts in secluded health posts; they worked during a specified shift only, typically with 'callback' duty once a week, should an emergency require additional midwifery staff. Cottage hospital midwives, furthermore, practised with the comfort of knowing that a ready supply of blood and general ward nurses were at hand for obstetrical emergencies, and that a doctor was nearby in case of medical problems. Appropriate equipment, too, allowed cottage hospital midwives to use skills acquired during formal vocational training. Yet, because the organisational structure of their workplace permitted discretion over the use of the technology, midwives never felt dominated by it. Finally, the cottage hospital created a number of managerial positions for experienced practitioners, while permitting the older generation of midwives to remain in close touch until retirement with ward colleagues as well as with pregnant women. The cottage hospital was perceived as ideal for midwives at *all* levels of the work hierarchy.

In brief, the cottage hospitals were attractive workplaces for midwives in many ways. Government salaries released midwives from economic dependence upon local inhabitants, many of whom were without adequate means to pay for services rendered. They were free from the dreaded 24-hour call and, moreover, had adequate access to emergency medical facilities and personnel, lifesaving technology and support staff—all assets absent from the work worlds of both their granny forerunners and rural dispensary counterparts. The small workforce of the maternity ward created a secure and relaxed atmosphere which fostered colleagueship among its predominantly midwifery staff. The cottage hospital also permitted a degree of work specialisation; while the granny women and health station midwives were frequently called upon to perform generalised nursing duties, cottage hospital midwives were able to orient their services mainly to the care of pregnant women and newborns. Their extended mandate, furthermore, helped to keep Caesarian sections, forceps deliveries and episiotomies at a minimum since they, not physicians, decided whether a labouring client needed obstetrical intervention. Finally, the cottage hospital created gateways for occupational mobility without isolating midwives in managerial positions from either pregnant women or lower-ranking colleagues.

Social change in Newfoundland and Labrador society in the mid-1960s, however, led to a challenge of the 'cottage concept' by health authorities. As part of a government scheme to encourage economic development, entire communities were resettled to so-called growth centres, where migrants were promised attractive full-time positions in yet-to-be established resource-extraction industries. When persuasion proved ineffective in stimulating resettlement, essential services were withdrawn.[5]

As a result of forced urbanisation and withdrawal of vital utilities from formerly well-established towns, the cottage hospital system declined. Medical and support staff left and were not replaced. Eventually even normal deliveries could no longer be safely performed on maternity wards. Unable to cope with the larger forces deciding their fate, unemployed cottage hospital midwives, along with their kin, packed their belongings and travelled in search of more promising habitats. The transplanted midwives had little choice but to seek employment in the new large hospitals, by then defined by health authorities as the only safe places for deliveries, with *doctors*, not midwives as the major attendants. Only in hinterland regions of Newfoundland and Labrador was midwifery allowed to survive. An era of midwifery practice in small organisations had drawn to a close, and with it a measure of professionalism had been lost that midwives have yet to win back.

BUREAUCRATIC EMPLOYMENT

Except in still intact towns in northern Newfoundland and Labrador, where doctors are in short supply and nurse-midwives retain legal status and conduct deliveries on small cottage hospitals wards, midwifery is not legal in Canada. Despite their formal qualifications and years of maternity ward experience, Newfoundland midwives have few work opportunities outside of bureaucratic employment. While most hold on to their occupational title of 'nurse-midwife,' they find themselves reduced to the position of obstetrical nurse, to the doctor's hand-maiden rather than an autonomous professional.

Of course, the regional and referral (teaching) hospitals, where the majority of present-day Newfoundland midwives work, have also brought benefits. Located in urban growth centres with a diverse citizenry, they provide access to well-equipped schools, shopping malls, recreation facilities, arts and culture centres, and movie theatres. In addition, the growth centres make available a variety of specialised services previously lacking in the settled towns and outports. Road and air transportation, too, is more efficient in the new growth areas. Most regional centres contain a vocational school, with telecommunication links to other institutions of higher education. Apart from these facilities, the urban atmosphere permits midwives to separate home and work environments, experiencing a level of privacy during off-duty times unknown even to the cottage hospital midwives.

On the surface, midwives in regional and referral hospitals appear to have attractive work roles. They serve a diversified clientele drawn from an extensive catchment area, leading to a regular supply of pregnant women on the maternity ward. They are likely to deal with a large group of middle-class clients with the inclination, time and resources to embrace the latest trends in prenatal care. Midwives in regional and referral hospitals, furthermore, find themselves in high-tech organisations that would seem to be a worker's dream. They are equipped with sophisticated birth equipment and distinguished by an advanced medical division of labour: on staff are obstetricians/gynecologists, pediatricians and anaesthetists, in addition to medical interns and residents handling off-hours emergencies. Sizeable maintenance crews make it unnecessary to perform the general nursing functions carried out by cottage hospital midwives during slack times on the maternity ward. Because of their diversified occupational structure, moreover, regional and referral hospitals potentially provide a considerable number of managerial positions. Finally, these large medical complexes draw students from a variety of health disciplines, promising midwifery employees attractive positions as informal ward instructors.

On close inspection, however, many of these seemingly positive organisational features *detract* from rather than enhance midwives' professionalism. Midwives now find themselves under the watchful eyes of hospital administrators implementing the latest bureaucratic management strategies to speed up work performance in an effort to cut staff numbers and remain within budgetary limits. As one regional hospital midwife comments:

> This hospital has gotten so big. I am not really a midwife anymore. Standards have changed and there is more and more administrative work: policy and procedures, accreditation, quality assurance are now the big things. A lot more red tape to go through and a lot more accountability to be made.

Regional and referral hospital midwives, like their cottage hospital counterparts, want to run the 'whole show' on the maternity ward, using their own discretion in calling upon neighbouring health occupations. Yet they find themselves in competition with doctors, nurses, and even students-in-training in the performance of midwifery tasks. Since physicians have usurped both normal and abnormal deliveries in these multifarious medical institutions, midwives have essentially become 'doctors' handmaidens.' They are pushed from centre stage and medical experts (sometimes even medical students!) perform the 'high-powered stuff.' In the words of one regional hospital midwife:

> Case room work is very frustrating! You are given no responsibility. You can't even deliver on your own. You see the whole thing—all the technology that's used, the inflexibility of birth.

As a result, the specialised knowledge and the skills of regional and referral hospital midwives are 'wasted.' Most midwives in these large sites of practice are extremely unhappy, maintaining that their medical rivals, as one referral hospital midwife bluntly states, "are often so focused on *extracting* the baby from the womb that they wouldn't know what a midwifery delivery looked like if it hit them in the face!"

Another outcome of these unfavourable circumstances is an increasing estrangement between staff midwives and the pregnant women under their care, many of whom must travel long distances to labour and deliver in a foreign environment.[6] As one regional hospital midwife explains:

> I mean, it puts you in a situation with your family being left for as high as four weeks, you in a hospital waiting for a baby. Is that NORMAL? They worry about their husband and children. And their social conditions are not middle-class Canada. So they have all the extra worries of social conditions. After two days of this woman in here, you don't bother to teach her anything! As long as she'll just stay here, she can just do as she likes.

Unlike their counterparts in the cottage hospitals, midwives in today's regional and referral hospitals, whether locals or immigrants, have little background knowledge of the vast majority of their clients. In interactions with labouring women, they tend, like the aloof scientist, 'to react with their heads instead of their hearts' (Merton [1949] 1957:569). An older midwife, with extensive cottage hospital experience to draw upon, comments:

> Many of the midwives [working in the regional hospital] are real greenhorns. It would be nice to have them even visit some of the women's homes, to know what they are going back to.

This is made worse by a lack of information about clients' due dates and by a harsh climate that frequently places land and air transportation on weather hold for extensive periods; this can lead to a situation where healthy pregnant women from distant communities are being institutionalised in regional and referral hospitals for several weeks both prior to and after deliveries. The new mothers feel lonely, apathetic and hostile as a result of forced confinement. As one referral hospital midwife observes:

> Many women get depressed. Bad enough coming here and going home with a new baby and having to cope with that, without being depressed even before you have it! And they do, they really do. The tears; I've never seen so many tears.

A growing indifference among institutionalised clients concerning the birth process is frequently the result. One former cottage hospital midwife explains that things were quite different during the earlier stages of her career:

> You don't get the same rapport with the women in the big hospital as was the case in the old cottage hospital. Now they don't seem to give as much. They just take it, just get it over with. Have the baby—that's it.

Although still relatively few in number, more politicised clients giving birth in these complex health establishments increasingly regard midwives' activities with suspicion, watchful for slip-ups that in serious cases could involve legal action.[7] Litigation, unknown a few decades ago, is now, as one referral hospital midwife points out, "becoming a real problem. That's what has spoiled the job for many midwives. They feel that everything must be written down, thinking all the while, will it stand up in court?"

In order to cope with heavy workloads and protect themselves from litigation, regional and referral hospital midwives increasingly rely upon elaborate monitoring and surveillance technology. It is precisely these devices, however, which create a wall that separates midwives from the birthing women, who tend to view their attendants as 'machine-minders,' as 'mechanical midwives,' rather than as service professionals genuinely interested in women's reproductive experiences. Midwives in the large hospitals are themselves well aware of their loss of personal contact with clients:

> It is too mechanical. We can do as much as eight epidurals a day and we are monitoring patients and we are busy putting on fetal scalp-electrodes. It is so BUSY! You just sort of push them in the labour room. Your brain ticks, but you are a 'mechanical midwife.'

There are yet other problems that affect present-day midwives. Rarely are they expected to fill in as substitute nurses on other wards; they instead confine their activities exclusively to maternity care. This seemingly positive development has not contributed to greater autonomy of the midwifery role, however. In fact, in contrast to the cottage hospital situation, little effort is now made to hire midwives specifically for maternity-care duty. Regional and referral hospital boards no longer give midwives preferential treatment over general nursing applicants or staff. There are consequently only a few midwives practising in each of the 15 large medical institutions, and they receive neither special monetary nor status rewards for their formal credentials. Such a small cohort of midwives in each setting leaves them professionally isolated; daily activities must be performed without the benefits of consultation with midwifery colleagues.

Regional and referral hospital midwives are also forced to compete with general nurses for senior appointments. No management positions on maternity wards are specifically designated for mature and experienced midwives. In fact, even midwives with impressive track records in the maternity-care field often find themselves managing hospital wards outside their own domain. One regional hospital midwife describes what she misses by overseeing a chronic care rather than maternity unit:

> I miss working with pregnant women. Right now I'm in a situation where I deal with a lot of death. At least when I was working in the case room, once the labour pains were over, it was a happy occasion, you see. You were dealing with the *living*, but now I tend to deal with the *dead*! Mind you, that has to be done too. But sometimes I tell myself that it's really very stupid to be dealing with all these problems. I should be downstairs dealing with life.

Frustrated by these constraints on their professional role, midwives at all levels of the hierarchy soon tend to become apathetic. A few venture northward and find employment in the surviving cottage hospitals located in the province's older towns. Most, however, stay on and come to view their bureaucratic career as a mere 'job.' Many opt for part-time employment. The more ambitious leave maternity work altogether, upgrading their formal nursing credentials by way of academic certification. They often redefine their career as being within the nursing profession, which holds out greater promise for professional achievement, including university teaching and research and hospital-based nursing schools instruction.

SUMMARY

My data on Newfoundland and Labrador midwives point to a considerable differentiation in regard to the professional status of midwives. The dark side of traditional homebirth attendance and clinic work—including 24-hour schedules, direct client and community control, lack of work specialisation, inadequate facilities, isolation from colleagues and absence of career mobility—has been largely ignored by writers critical of present-day service employ-ment. Midwives in bureaucratic hospitals subject to continuous supervision by medical specialists and administrators and separated from birthing women by complex technology, have also suffered from a lack of autonomy. Only midwives employed in the cottage hospitals managed to gain a considerable measure of control over their work activities. As will become clear in Chapter 4, the cottage hospital site was crucial in helping midwives to acquire the art and science of their occupation.

Balancing Art and Science: **4**
Schooling and Socialisation
of Midwives

> *Midwifery is a science but it's also an art. And what's been happen-*
> *ing over the years is that the art is getting lost and the science is*
> *coming to the forefront.*
>
> Vocationally-trained Midwife

Newfoundland and Labrador midwives highlight autonomy at work
and successful acquisition of specialised maternity-care knowledge
as well as long-term commitment to clients as crucial for professionalism. Most modern writers on service occupations also grant
these features priority in their analyses. There, nevertheless,
remains strong disagreement concerning the best way of organising
these attributes in preparing recruits for professional practice.
Adopting the professionalisation thesis, for example, some
sociologists have maintained that universities provide an ideal
training ground (Parsons 1951; Merton 1957). Yet feminists (Rothman 1982; Greer 1984) and other social critics (Becker *et al.* 1961,
1968; Illich 1971), endorsing the deprofessionalisation thesis, have
tended to reject 'university diploma mills,' which, they maintain,
block rather than enhance knowledge acquisition. Many have even
called for a return to the type of apprenticeship common during the
traditional era, when novices received extensive practical training
and village inhabitants still had a major role to play in the recruitment of lay practitioners to service roles (Illich 1971; Bowles & Gintis
1976).

    This chapter attempts to shed light on this controversy by
examining the training and socialisation of Newfoundland and
Labrador midwives in historical perspective. Three styles of prepara-

tion—apprenticeship, vocational training and academic education —can be discerned from my interview data. In comparison to both apprenticeship and academic styles, vocational instruction nicely blended the art and science of midwifery to produce competent and committed graduates dedicated to serving pregnant women. As will become clear below, the vocationally-trained midwife was able to employ her specialised knowledge to a degree not enjoyed by either her lay predecessors, her clinic counterparts, or her contemporary equivalents in bureaucratic settings. Her advantage lay in her access to an innovative institution—the cottage hospital.

THE TRADITIONAL APPRENTICESHIP SYSTEM

In traditional Newfoundland and Labrador, as in most premodern societies, attending women in childbirth was in principle the province of older married or widowed women who had themselves borne many children (Donegan 1978; Wertz & Wertz 1977; Donnison 1977).

Most granny midwives maintain that only female attendants can adequately care for pregnant women, providing sustained personalised care throughout the lying-in period. Females, in their view, are by nature warm and expressive, while males tend to be innately cool and instrumental. Women are endowed with the special gift of compassionate understanding, making them ideal midwives.[1] Grannies also note that their clients displayed modesty concerning reproductive matters, and felt shame in exposing themselves in front of males. The female midwife served as a kind of protector of the pregnant woman, attempting to keep the events surrounding her personal passage through birth secret. In the words of one granny midwife:

> It don't seem nice for a man to go in and watch everything, the after-birth coming and all like that. It don't seem really nice to me. It's all right for a woman, 'cause a woman understands it all. In my time, they left it up to women and we would handle it ourselves.

Female status was merely one condition for recruitment as midwife. As is the case for traditional healers elsewhere (Fabrega & Silver 1970; Fabrega 1971), Newfoundland and Labrador lay midwives were ideally not 'young upstarts'; they were expected to embark upon independent practice (after a long period of apprenticeship) only toward the end of their own reproductive cycle, around age 40, and to continue work into their octogenarian years. Local inhabitants believed that the midwife accumulated a stock of wisdom with increasing age—hence the term 'wise woman' in several

European languages, or 'auntie' or 'granny woman,' as she was affectionately known in Newfoundland and Labrador. The *sage-femme* or granny midwife, ideally, was an older, mature woman, though perhaps illiterate, who was seen as the 'salt of the earth.' In some cases she was revered as a kind of charismatic leader, an elder, especially after long years of altruistic service to pregnant women and their families. This observation parallels the finding of high community status enjoyed by successful black U.S. granny midwives (Mongeau *et al.* 1961; Auerbach 1968; Holmes 1986).

In addition to knowledge rooted in gender and age, granny women had firsthand experience of the reproductive process. The fact that she had given birth to several children was a crucial rite of passage that provided her with unmediated knowledge of parturition. Motherhood, it was believed, helped grannies to take the role of the other, to really know the pains and joys of clients, to gain an insider's view of the birthing process.

Various aspects of the traditional lay midwife's everyday knowledge were shared by most women in the community, just like the skills of housekeeping, caring for children and kin, and familiarity with home cures. The granny midwife, however, was also thought to possess a 'special know-how,' which, by way of informal apprenticeship, was passed on by a seasoned teacher of the midwifery craft. It was this additional body of singular practical knowledge, then, that distinguished the traditional lay midwife from local women without apprenticeship training for the roles of community birth attendant and healer.

Prototypically, too, the granny midwives were 'called' to their work and 'destined' to become maternity workers; a mysterious power, it was believed, recruited them at an early age to the office of midwife and placed them under the care of close female kin, typically a granny mother, aunt, or grandmother, who would act as chaperon and guide until completion of the apprenticeship training. If need be, one of the 'Lord's messengers'—a travelling priest, clergy or doctor—would remind the 'chosen one' of her role as caregiver:

> I always enjoyed public life and community work. At an early age I started visiting the sick and aged. My life ambition was to be a nurse and midwife after I learned some things about obstetrics from my mother, who had also been a midwife. [Later] I delivered several babies in emergencies. Then the travelling doctor asked if I could help him out. I told him that he would have to help me out if I got into any hard scrapes and he said, 'well, you do your best for me and I'll do my best for you.' So that's how it all started.

While there was neither a formal educational prerequisite nor a designated age at which a local woman could begin her actual apprenticeship, the onset of occupational socialisation ideally commenced in her late teens or early twenties. Initially, the neophyte was expected to demonstrate competence in performing such arduous tasks as washing, cleaning, and cooking meals for the expectant mother's family during the typical 10-day lying-in period. In addition, the trainee learned how to sterilise rudimentary instruments in a pan of boiling water at the back of the stove, and to take care of the newborn, for example, by tying the umbilical cord with a small piece of linen and protecting it with the 'dried flour' she had been instructed to brown in the oven. Eventually, the novice was permitted to independently visit the woman in labour, spending long nights at the expectant mother's bedside until the birth was imminent and the senior granny kinswoman took control. The apprentice watched her teacher in action, noting how she encouraged the labouring woman to 'work with the pain' while both held hands and waited for 'nature to do its work.' She also heard her teacher tell the client 'not to scream too much but to bear down,' that with lots of 'oil and patience' and 'prayers to the Mother of Perpetual Help to guide them,' everything would soon be normal again. The apprentice observed the granny midwife in difficult obstetrical cases — twin deliveries, breech and vertex presentations, footlings, mild pre-eclampsia — and learned about serious complications requiring medical help. During such training sessions the novice picked up paediatric skills as well, for example rubbing premature infants with oil, wrapping them in flannelette and, when not at their mother's breast, laying them in a warm bed surrounded by hot bricks until normal weight had been reached. Finally, the trainee learned to care for the birthing woman and her family during the postpartum period, advising the new mother on breastfeeding her infant — except if her milk was 'blue.'[2]

The apprenticeship system did not merely transmit practical skills. It also ideally transmitted important cultural values. Apprentices were familiarised with traditional rituals and rules of midwifery practice, such as how to properly discard the afterbirth by wrapping it in an old sheet and throwing it in the hot stove, how to console bereaved family members in the event of injury or death of a newborn or mother, and how to baptise and prepare the deceased for burial whenever the travelling priest or minister was absent from the community. In addition, birth attendance in clients' homes placed the trainee face-to-face with the economic and social problems of her future clientele. She watched how the senior midwife insightfully adapted her practices to the needs of the pregnant woman, which, as one granny midwife explains, were sometimes desperate indeed:

> I expected clean sheets and towels. Over there in the merchant families everything would be perfect. But in some places you'd go, there would not even be anything to eat and only one sheet on the bed and that would be it. I'd born the baby and then take the sheet, wash it, and put it back on the bed again, and I'd use my own sheet to wrap the baby.

Once she had mastered the necessary practical skills and compassionate understanding, the trainee was permitted to carry out pre- and postnatal visits and to respond to night calls on her own, as well as to fill in for her teacher when she was busy with another client. Finally, the apprentice became an independent practitioner in her own right, an informally certified lay midwife capable of guiding new recruits through the lengthy schooling process. One granny midwife, whose grandmother and mother were also traditional lay midwives, describes her own career, which spanned five decades:

> I used to go with my grandmother and...just watched. I was there when a woman used to be sick. Grandmother used to bring the stuff and sterilise it. I had four children before I really started. I delivered my first baby for my sister when she took sick before her time. I had everything ready for the time the midwife come, just waiting for her. But the baby come and I took the string and I tied the little stomach and tied the other part. Now the midwife come and she said: "My dear, you done it better than I can," 'cause she was getting old. And then, from that, they used to come after me. One to the other, one to the other. One time I was three weeks never stopped. Oh yes, I enjoyed it while I was at it. I was getting my old age pension when I gave it up.

The apprenticeship system, in theory, produced mature, wise and experienced granny midwives committed to working in their home communities. This original method of occupational grounding was, however, beset by serious problems. Like her outport[3] counterparts of both genders who were required by circumstance to commence adult work roles at a tender age, trainees were sometimes expected to abort the initial stages of carefree childhood which today are considered crucial for full human development. The premature onset of one granny midwife's apprenticeship training represents an extreme:

> I almost born one when I was eight years old! My father was out trapping and I never hardly had the sense to know that my mother was going to have a child. She was upstairs. Not very often she

[would] go upstairs. And I heard a groan and another groan. At last she bawled out: 'go get the pan, heat some salt and water, get the scissors, heave boiling water over them and bring it up to me in a hurry.' I did all that and I got halfway up the stairs when my father come in. He said: 'don't go in'! He took the basin and he went up. He wasn't hardly upstairs when I heard the baby crying. Oh, I had to learn so young, hey.

Hasty recruitment was, of course, an outcome of the constant shortage of traditional lay midwives. In fact, as the above respondent experienced first-hand, *male* birth attendants—fathers, uncles, sons—had sometimes to be recruited, despite rural women's preference for female attendants. As one granny midwife explains:

You see, if the mother got caught and there was no midwife or woman helper then it was whoever was around, even a man. My father had to do it and my uncle, uncle Willie, he delivered some of his own children. The men did help if a hand was needed, but they didn't like washing babies and things like that. Men didn't like that. The mothers preferred to have one of us to look after her but you couldn't always get enough to train. You had to have somebody who was not nervous about those things. I guess it was alright to have a man, if he was not the nervous type. But most wouldn't have anything to do with it if they could help it.

Many traditional lay midwives learned to perform midwifery tasks by *necessity* and not (as was usually the case for the next generation of vocationally-trained midwives), in response to an inner calling or an authentic desire to attend expectant mothers. There simply 'was no one else to tend to sick women.' While some who entered midwifery via this route subsequently developed genuine commitment, many felt trapped in an arduous work role bringing little personal reward. One young respondent recalls the situation of her own granny mother:

I can remember as a kid someone pounding on the door in the middle of the night and Dad [later] saying that Mom had gone to deliver a baby and would be back in two days. There was another older lady [but] she was probably in her seventies by that time. My mom was the only person available and she felt a certain responsibility. She couldn't bear the thought of somebody having to deliver on their own, and this would have happened, you know. Or somebody who had no experience would have been present—in cases where the baby was corded and if the cord had been cut before the baby was delivered, then the baby would have died...But I think if she had a choice she probably would have never got into it. It was very much a matter that there was nobody else available. Now she says she has lost her nerve, and can't bear the thought of doing those things, that even [the sight of] blood just really bothers her.

The apprenticeship system, based on the assumption that age increases 'wisdom knowledge' through experience, also lacked a formal mechanism to eliminate incompetence, especially among aging granny midwives whose practical skills and hygienic habits were no longer up to par.[4] Although none of them were accused of witchcraft or of being in league with the devil—a common event for lay midwives practising in medieval Europe (Donnison 1977)—all granny respondents, nevertheless, did single out one or two of their equals in neighbouring communities as 'ignorant' and 'unclean.' Consequently, some clients were the victims of the unsound birth rituals of senile grannies who stubbornly resisted retirement. One granny midwife recalls how she lost her infant son in this way:

> I had trouble with the midwife 'cause she didn't help me. He had his little arm like that, and she didn't know how to get him. Well, I come out of it but he didn't. See, she was getting old then. I sooner had someone else 'cause she didn't handle things right.

As noted above, many apprenticeship-trained granny midwives possessed a remarkable understanding of the socio-economic and cultural circumstances of their clientele, in addition to practical skills in dealing with normal pregnancy and childbirth. Their isolated rural existence, however, deprived even the most competent granny midwives of access to the up-to-date knowledge about what to do in the case of obstetrical abnormalities and prevented them from mastering important technical skills acquired from handling life-saving medical equipment. Most grannies were content to simply continue with the traditional apprenticeship system:

> I never had that attitude to go on in school and learn that way. We had the old-fashioned feelings. We made the mothers stay in bed for 10 days and we'd go collect different things for medicine to heal the mothers. Juniper and things like that for infection and kidney trouble. The way we was used to was the old-fashioned way.

Yet, like many modern lay midwives (Weitz & Sullivan 1985:40–1), some grannies longed to improve their limited knowledge, to learn new ways of reducing frequent pregnancies and preventing deaths, instead of merely appealing to the 'mercy of the Lord.' As one of them recounts:

> Experience was our teacher; we didn't have no other. I think we learned a lot by experience but, like labours that were very long, you just had to wait and see what would happen. We didn't know what to do; just give them a cup of tea. I wanted to know the whole

works, to know if they get sick we could do something for that and not always just let nature have its way. Maybe it was better in some ways [than today], but not if you needed to have an operation or anything like that. I wanted to know it all. Like before the time come for their baby or if they get fever or anything, I'd know what to do. I wanted to get away to learn.

Traditional lay midwives, even those schooled by way of a lengthy apprenticeship system, were committed and competent maternity workers only in a limited sense. Some possessed practical skills and a dedication to serving clients, others were incompetent, and many became midwives without ever experiencing midwifery as a calling or desiring to work with pregnant women. Furthermore, since they lacked crucial obstetrical knowledge, they often did not know when to call for the travelling doctor, if in reach, or when to transport a client to the nearest hospital. And their lack of technical skills in handling life-saving equipment made it virtually impossible for them to aid the doctor during times of abnormalities. In brief, the traditional apprenticeship system fell short of preparing midwives for *professional* practice. In an effort to overcome the drawbacks of this original style of occupational instruction, a new type of vocational preparation emerged in the early decades of the 20th century.

VOCATIONAL TRAINING

The apprenticeship system remained intact until the second decade of the 20th century, when state-financed pronatalist policies were introduced in Newfoundland and Labrador. As previously noted, government concern for child welfare and public health in the post-World War I period prompted legislation requiring the registration of every birth. Limited public funds were available for philanthropic groups to establish milk depots, health clinics and maternity hospitals.[5] In addition, funds were allotted to employ foreign doctors and vocationally-trained nurses and midwives recruited mainly from Commonwealth countries. These come-from-away midwives set up clinics in rural areas and among the urban poor. After the 1930s, many were recruited to posts in the emerging cottage hospitals and others to teaching positions in the new midwifery courses offered to granny midwives and young local students.

This innovative vocational style of instructing and socialising aspirants to the role of midwife was remarkably different from the earlier apprenticeship system. Methods of recruitment, for example, underwent substantial change, for the first time opening up a career line for those younger, unmarried women who demonstrated a keen commitment to this line of work. Although all granny midwives were encouraged to upgrade their lay credentials, there was an increasing tendency to recruit literate single women professing a calling to midwifery who, unlike their traditional lay counterparts, were not 'set in their ways' and thus more willing to accept the new scientific aspects of midwifery training taught at the hospital school.[6] One vocationally-trained midwife, now retired, explains why she was chosen by her community:

> When I was born here there wasn't any midwife trained then. We always had just old women—you know, granny women, as they called them. [When I was young], my grandmother was a good granny midwife. There were two or three others. But when I came out, they were getting too old to do any work. I always liked helping people but I never done any midwifery before I trained. I was always a *trained* midwife. Father Thomas asked me to go to the school in St. John's. They wanted to get someone young, not an old person. An awful lot of old grannies who went into the school, who were doing this work for years, were so set in their ways that they wasn't going to do anything the teachers talked about.

By situating vocational training in the maternity hospital, students gained access to a continuous flow of pregnant women on the ward. This had not been so in the traditional apprenticeship system based on one-to-one interaction between the granny midwife and her homebirth client. The vocational novice was presented with the unique opportunity of being able to observe many labours and deliveries within a relatively short time span and in a controlled environment. This helped her to adopt a rational and matter-of-fact perspective on the birthing process which the lay apprentice had viewed as belonging to the domain of 'God and Nature' and had been sanctioned by the expectant mother's family and the local community. In grasping this novel perspective on the female reproductive cycle, the vocational student learned when safe medical intervention in the labour process was possible and desirable, both to ease childbirth pain and to safeguard the life of infants and mothers. The novice was instructed to discard such ancient notions held by many granny midwives as the conviction that women's suffering during childbirth was due to 'Eve's Curse.' She was encouraged to adopt a thoroughly secular view of the causes of abnormality in labour. In brief, during vocational preparation, students learned to *predict* complications and to alert the doctor if necessary.

Thorough maternity training was hardly possible in the short training course of two or three months then offered by the vocational programs (Nevitt 1978). In both the Midwives' and the integrated

Maternity Nursing Course, established in the mid-1920s at the two maternity hospitals, the formal education component was limited since the student midwife was expected to 'learn while doing,' to test theoretical insights while performing general duties on the maternity ward. In exchange for a meagre stipend that covered her room and board, the trainee had to squeeze lectures and study periods into her few hours of time 'free' from a gruelling work shift. This situation, accompanied by strict boarding house rules, meant that the student had little social life.

Gradually, these conditions improved, however. The lecture schedule was extended to six months, and there were added opportunities for clinical experience with expectant mothers at all stages of their reproductive cycle. House rules and dress codes were relaxed and time was allotted for leisure activities (Nevitt 1978). A balance was struck between the transmission of theoretical knowledge and its application as well as between schooling and social life. As one vocationally-trained midwife maintains:

> The beauty of vocational training was that there was a lot of theory but you learned it by relating it to what you were actually *seeing* and relating with. I can't see that you can learn much away from the environment you're learning about. You learned something in the classroom but then you went to the ward and saw it in practice. You know, relating theory to practice was essential. We didn't just learn from textbooks.

Midwifery [in the vocational program] was not just theoretical training. In this sense, the vocational student gained access to 'esoteric knowledge' through active participation in the relatively enclosed worlds of hospital school and maternity ward.[7] Here is the personal story of an early graduate:

> I was 32. I packed my bags and went to St. John's. They had a boarding house for us near the school. I went in the first day; I was told, 'come on, there's a case on.' So we had to take a mask and go into the case room. Oh, I felt like coming home! It was so foreign to me; I thought it was just terrible. But when I saw the baby's head, it gave me a different feeling. I wanted to stay there then, to see the end of it... We had to go down to clinic every Tuesday and Thursday. Women used to come for their check-ups and the doctor used to teach us how to find the baby, where the baby was lying, how to find the heart beats and all this. The midwives would tell us how to check the person for examination... After it was over, I got a licence. I was a licensed practising midwife.

Vocational training required not just acquisition of formal knowledge and new obstetrical techniques. In anticipation of her future role of a practitioner able to utilise 'hands, heart and mind,' the student-in-training, like her granny forerunner, was also expected to familiarise herself with the social and cultural background of her outport clientele. Midwifery teachers, many of whom had practised in rural communities and town hospitals in Britain and Commonwealth countries early on in their careers, drew upon their own practical experience and instilled in students the dedication of servicing poor, uneducated, native and rural clients just as well as urban clients and those of higher social-economic standing. As one vocationally-trained midwife explains:

> When we was in training, [our teachers]would tell us stories about their experiences around the place and what to expect when we got home, how things were when you went to different houses, that in some places people had everything you wanted but in other places you just had to improvise with different things, which was true. Some houses had everything and others nothing at all.

It testifies to the success of the vocational midwifery program that, according to vocationally-trained respondents, most of their classmates did in fact eventually practise as maternity attendants, many returning to their home community or to an adjacent one, providing an important service to city, town and rural populations alike. These trained midwives, with their up-dated midwifery bags and a Midwives' Manual to consult in case of emergency,[8] gradually replaced the aging granny midwives trained by way of informal apprenticeship.

The new vocational instruction was able to overcome one of the major drawbacks of the apprenticeship system by institutionalising rules to deal with incompetence. The vocational graduate was a government-certified practitioner, required to register all births with the Central Midwives' Board, to record the particulars of each labour and delivery and, moreover, to keep in close contact with the district supervisor—typically a senior midwife or sometimes a regional nurse or doctor. Under the 1920 'Midwives Act', the Supervisor of Midwives was invested with the power to discipline all colleagues practising under her jurisdiction, and, should a misdeed be serious enough, to call for the withdrawal of their midwifery permits and the elimination of their name from the annually updated Midwives' Roll. Such a penalty might be involved if, for example, a midwife knowingly refused to attend a distressed client or acted in a wrongful manner during a delivery. Vocational training, then, was accompanied by formal procedures that permitted the removal of incompetent and uncommitted practitioners, thereby providing relatively consistent maternity care to clients.

Nevertheless, as long as homebirth and rural clinic practice remained the norm, many older granny midwives, with or without vocational training, continued to practise in the traditional ways and remained skeptical about the benefits of the new midwifery. One granny midwife who underwent both types of schooling maintains that "the midwifery course didn't teach me anything I didn't already know." There is more than a germ of truth in her statement since even vocational graduates, without a career option other than isolated home or clinic practice, had to place much of their knowledge acquired during schooling on hold. Like their lay forerunners, they had no easy access to doctors and medical technology nor a way to improve the poor working conditions typical of small-scale sites of practice.

But gradually a new work site—the cottage hospital—gained a prominent role in maternity care, allowing the vocationally-trained midwife an opportunity to use her specialised knowledge and technical skills to a far greater degree than previously possible in either home settings or health stations. The result was continuity between vocational preparation and cottage hospital work, between knowledge transmitted during formal training and postgraduate socialisation.

The regionalisation of maternity-care services in the past few decades has virtually eliminated these attractive work sites, however, in favour of large-scale bureaucratic hospitals characterised by a focus on high technology and by medical dominance of maternity-care delivery. These changes have been accompanied by a substantial modification of midwives' occupational instruction as well. Vocational instruction has increasingly been replaced by 'maternity nursing.' Once the earlier vocational courses in midwifery had become defunct, candidates were now trained as doctors' obstetrical assistants, receiving only a few months of additional maternity course work on a regional or referral hospital maternity ward but typically little delivery experience and no community practice at all. Obstetric nurses are officially regarded in these large-scale hospitals on a par with vocationally-trained midwives, and are awarded a comparable salary.

One of the outcomes of this turn of events has been growing client dissatisfaction with the organisation of pregnancy and childbirth.[9] The regionalisation of maternity-care services not only has resulted in the erosion of vocational schooling for local recruits and the elimination of a relatively autonomous site of midwifery practice; it has also lowered the quality of maternity-care for certain types of clients who are forced to spend long periods away from their families and friends and under the care of attendants in large high-tech hospitals with little knowledge of their personal backgrounds.

Rather than recreating vocational preparation and regenerating the dying cottage hospital system, provincial health authorities began in the early 1970s to encourage the establishment of a university-based academic midwifery program that could meet the special needs of pregnant women.[10]

ACADEMIC EDUCATION

The academisation of Newfoundland and Labrador midwifery[11] is closely intertwined with the bureaucratisation of maternity-care services. The regional and referral hospitals that began to emerge in the late 1960s have virtually eliminated the role of the professional midwife, except in surviving cottage hospitals. Increasing medical dominance of maternity care and the technological orientation of these large hospitals has reduced the role of most practising midwives to that of hand-maiden/technocrat—a 'mechanical midwife.' In contrast to the cottage hospitals, where vocationally-trained midwives were able to keep their skills honed through practice on small wards organised around a midwifery model of maternity care, present-day complex medical establishments have divided obstetrics into major specialised components—prenatal, labour, delivery and postpartum—delegating its atomised midwifery work-force to one of these specific areas. The continuity of labour and delivery has inevitably become broken, resulting for many midwives in the experience of alienation from their work.

This is the organisational structure now encountered by midwifery educators. Many of them previously held instructor positions in the bygone vocational programs and only recently upgraded their credentials in order to meet university prerequisites for a teaching position in the Nursing School. Initially the Nursing School had objected to the academisation of midwifery education. In the 1970s, however, it agreed to design a midwifery specialty within the academic nursing program. It was hoped that competent and committed midwife graduates would seek employment in the few remaining cottage hospitals of the northern districts as well in peripheral health stations afflicted with a persistent turnover of midwifery personnel.

The university-based program has faced formidable barriers. Even before the new specialty could get off the ground, there was the problem of finding field placements for its students. With the erosion of most cottage hospitals, an important institution of clinical training for neophyte midwives was all but eliminated. While some midwives-in-training managed to find placements in the few remaining cottage hospitals, limited space in these institutions has forced many to look elsewhere for practical experience. The existing alter- native clinical sites — the regional and referral hospitals — remain in heavy demand from students in other health occupations, in par- ticular nursing and medicine. A precipitous fall in rural as well as urban birth rates (five or more live births per woman was the provincial norm until the late 1960s; today's reproductive rate is below the Canadian figure of 1.7 live births per woman) has wor- sened the situation. Family physicians and obstetricians, having replaced cottage hospital midwives as primary birth attendants, are increasingly unwilling to step aside and allow midwifery students to deliver *their* maternity clients.

In the face of such intense competition for clinical training, midwifery educators have been compelled to go abroad in search of placement of a few candidates per year in a small maternity hospital in the north of Scotland — the 'Scottish connection,' as it has come to be called. However, most students do not have the economic resources to finance such a costly, if attractive, clinical semester on the other side of the Atlantic. Faced with this situation, midwifery educators eventually decided to join the trend among other health disciplines of deemphasising practical experience, instead evaluat- ing progress largely in conventional academic terms: marks on short-answer quizzes and on a final examination, in addition to writing up a community project designed to test ability to carry out scholarly research rather than practical competence.

Modelling their expectations on the cottage hospital vocational programs of former decades, university midwifery educators had hoped to attract a large pool of native-born applicants desiring to do maternity work in the province. Much to their surprise, however, recruitment from less-advantaged groups has remained very low. The stringent formal entrance requirements and the program's heavy academic emphasis, it seems, discourage the application of many potential candidates interested in midwifery. One midwifery educator observes:

> How to get local people to come? Some of the universities [in other Western areas] have special programs to orient students from rural communities and small towns into the educational system. But if they want to be professionals, then they have to be able to say: 'I'm no different than any other midwife.'

Substantial tuition fees, no doubt, have exacerbated the recruit- ment problem. Less-privileged candidates, especially those from outside the capital city unable to live comparatively cheaply at home, have been prevented from applying for economic reasons. Moreover, unlike in the vocational school, the university requires all its students to pay for their acquired knowledge in cash rather than, as was previously the case for vocational recruits, in *labour*—by working part-time on the maternity ward.

In brief, the university's admission policy, with its stress on high school grade point averages and mastery of a standardised liberal arts curriculum, and its complete deemphasis of an intimate knowledge of the socio-cultural backgrounds of clients, has discouraged many potential students. Substantial tuition fees only augment the problem. The university, as a result, has virtually eliminated from serious competition the very pool of aspirants from which the now defunct vocational midwifery programs recruited the majority of their candidates.

Clinical experience and recruitment have not been the only stumbling blocks in successfully academising midwifery. Many of the students who manage to overcome these formidable initial barriers express dissatisfaction about the lack of practice-orientation in their training; they maintain that the program's emphasis upon esoteric scientific theory to the detriment of crucial hands-on midwifery skills is both unnecessarily demanding and to a large extent irrelevant. One student even suggests that the program is a 'bit of a sham.' Although this may be a harsh judgement, it may well be true that many of the students who cannot easily master academic courses would nevertheless be competent and committed midwives. In the words of a student who failed the course:

> I've done this midwifery course and my marks aren't high enough to get my midwifery certificate. But where do the marks come from? It's all *academics*! When I got my marks back I called my instructor and she told me that in my community project I had not followed the proper format for the references in the back. I said: 'What has that got to do with midwifery?' First I'm told that I failed my exams because I didn't write down the proper brackets, quotation marks, and whatever, and then I'm told that I have to repeat the Practical. The two just didn't make any sense. What I've learned this year was a lot, lot more than anything that was put on those exams ... I don't see how they can teach midwifery in a university setting. I think it's outrageous.

Vocationally-trained midwives, many of whom previously worked in cottage hospitals and are now employed in the regional and referral hospitals where they come into contact with university midwifery students, have also criticised the program's academic emphasis on the grounds that it divorces midwifery theory from practice and produces graduates without the practical skills crucial for good client care. In the words of one such practitioner:

> Vocational training is far better because you're in the obstetric hospital for the midwifery and you do the whole caboodle together. You get your theory and everything rolled into one, and it sinks in better. But[at the university] it's separate. The theory is thrown at them! You want a lot of hands-on in normals and abnormals in order to see what you read about in texts. [The university students] can deliver. But they've missed out on a lot. You need to train on all the wards:antenatal, postnatal and delivery. And then two years of post-graduate work in the hospital. You've got everything you need then.

Another vocationally-trained midwife, a recent immigrant familiar with a similar British academic program, maintains that academic education forces recruits to concentrate on 'assessing' clients, while their bedside needs often go unmet:

> I'm prejudiced to the [vocational program] ... While I was in training, the girls from the university would come and be allotted to the same ward. While we were running around and attending to the patients' needs, they were 'assessing' and thinking about 'mental status.' [Yet] a patient was in there in bed and uncomfortable and in pain. First of all, I would sort that all out and then I would do the psychology. They did it the other way around!

Or, in the words of a retired cottage hospital midwife:

> You couldn't beat the hospital-trained midwives. They had a close contact with the patients. Just the little extra things that they thought about doing for their patients that the university graduate wouldn't. She's the more "academic type," hey. She's got it up here, but she can't put it [into practice]. Now, somebody has got to do the bedside care, right?

A substantial minority of vocationally-trained midwives in fact go so far as to claim that, without crucial practical skills and sympathetic understanding, university graduates are potentially *dangerous* to the women placed under their care. "I cringe when I see them come with that university education," one of them proclaims, and another bluntly professes: "I'm a *practical* trained midwife. We do our training on the ward. What's university, university, university, when you're cleaning out a bedpan or at a patient's bedside giving them support? University don't mean *squat* then!"

Midwifery educators, not surprisingly, have taken exception to such strong criticism from students and vocationally-trained midwives, pointing instead to the many positive aspects of an academic education, such as the freedom granted to students from demanding work schedules during their studies. One educator recalls her own vocational training, asserting that in crucial ways it fell short of its present-day academic replacement:

> Sometimes I wish that I had been able to be an observer I remember the students from the university. Their tutors would come. It was one hectic morning. They would take them away for their electives. We didn't have any time to do that because we were workers; we were hospital staff, and we envied them that. If there was something going on that we should be experiencing—perhaps it was a once-in-a-life-time thing—if it was busy on the ward, then we couldn't go but they could. We were extra staff; they were students.

Midwifery educators also point to the advantaged position of their students whose residence is separate from their place of learning, who have easy access to state-of-the-art libraries and a wide choice of courses in the biological and social sciences, and who enjoy the excitement which can come with studying alongside students from other branches of higher education. According to midwifery educators, all this provided students with the opportunity to acquire valuable communication and counselling skills as well as with the chance to practise independent thought:

> Vocational students were 'thrown to the wolves' and sometimes had to take responsibility long before they were intellectually ready for it. I must say, the [vocational] system gave direction, clear, specific direction so that graduates always knew the process of how to get from there to there to there. But you could never slacken off, to develop more independence of thinking.This is the big value of the university education: that the student is not sort of hemmed in by learning within the system, which is, of course, stultifying to ideas.

The academic program has undoubtedly been successful in some respects. It has produced midwives for managerial positions, in addition to researchers and instructors. And the location of midwifery education in the university has enhanced midwives' political position vis-à-vis other service workers, including doctors. One midwifery educator contends that the program "has given students more of a political awareness [than vocational training]. They have been able to talk to physicians on most things because they have a university degree too."

How successful has academic education been in preparing practitioners competent in the art and science of midwifery, and committed to providing altruistic service to clients? The fact remains that few university graduates have embarked upon maternity work. Peripheral health stations remain understaffed; the few academic graduates who have ventured there have stayed at most two years before returning to urban areas in search for bureaucratic employment or further credentials at the university. This outcome is hardly surprising. What is surprising, however, is that graduates have completely failed to secure positions in the remaining cottage hospitals, where midwifery is still the dominant model of care. One reason for this abysmal showing has been the student's lack of both *practical skill* and *socio-cultural knowledge* of the types of clients served by the cottage hospitals. Even academic educators—most of whom, after all, hold vocational as well as university credentials and previously practised on cottage hospital wards—have been forced to admit that a chasm remains between the expertise of the vocationally-trained midwife and her university counterpart. Some have suggested that if students were to be initially educated as baccalaureate nurses and only later to specialise in midwifery at the M.A. level, this major lack in competence and commitment to maternity practice might be overcome. But most educators and virtually all practitioners tend to believe otherwise. An older vocationally-trained midwife who, prior to her present regional hospital managerial position worked for two decades in a cottage hospital observes:

> Really, I have nothing against BNs or any [university] degree. I'm all for it. But I really feel that we have lost our perspective. Theoretically, [university students] have the learning, the education. They seem to have all the answers. But when it comes to dealing with the patient in a situation, they don't have the practical experience. They are excellent girls but removed from the patient. They have their formal education, their BNs and now they're getting their Masters.' Okay, we need administrators. But the standard of care has gone down since I started work in 1952. This is what is lacking.

Given these various deep-seated problems, it is hardly surprising that the midwifery specialty is now under investigation and some midwifery teachers fear that the program, after a mere decade or so of fledgling existence, may be dropped altogether in the near future.

SUMMARY

It remains uncertain whether the present-day reformation of midwifery schooling in the direction of greater academic credentialling will increase the number of competent and committed midwives available for practitioner roles. The university's emphasis upon high school grade point averages and mastery of abstract theoretical material, in addition to the substantial tuition fees, bars recruitment of students possessing a spirit of dedication to maternity work but who lack economic resources and may not be 'university material.' But this is only part of the problem. An attractive clinical site (such as the cottage hospitals in their heyday), where neophytes can apply their newly acquired midwifery theory, does not exist. In brief, a major restructuring of maternity-care delivery in favour of small organisations, like the mothercare centres today in Sweden's cities and towns, is urgently needed, where practitioners can blend the art and science of midwifery without fear of encroachment from administrators and doctors.

Some of the social policy implications of these findings will be discussed in the next chapter.

Searching for a Middle Ground: Midwifery in Small Organisations

The ideal would be something small, something in-between, where the midwife and mother can have the best of both worlds. You're really out on a limb delivering alone. I mean, birth at home can be fine if it's all natural and nice. But once a complication sets in, it's very dangerous, you see, and the woman gets the worst end of the stick. [On the other hand], large maternity units are so mechanised that you can't get close to the patient. You're all the time machine-minding and charting so that your knowledge gets stale and you miss the contact with the women.

Cottage Hospital Midwife

Comparative analysis of birthing systems in five advanced industrial countries—Sweden, the Netherlands, Britain, the United States, Canada—discloses significant diversity of organisational and occupational structures across and even within national boundaries. Disquiet among midwives and pregnant women concerning local conditions is apparent in several of the countries examined. Research on childbirth management in present-day Sweden and my own data on the historical transformation of midwifery in Newfoundland and Labrador point to the variability of midwifery in small health organisations where a delicate balance, it seems, can be maintained between the preference of clients for safety and personal attention and a substantial degree of professionalism for midwives. Such a balance has typically not been achieved in either homecare or bureaucratic organisations. The professionalism achieved by midwives in relatively non-bureaucratic organisational settings has generally been overlooked even by critics of present-day American and British birthing systems.

This is not to suggest that the literature that emphasises the subordinate role of female service employees subjected to medical and bureaucratic forms of control is without analytic value. Those midwives in my study working in large hospitals under conditions of medical dominance certainly articulate alienation from both co-workers and clients and point to a lack of genuine opportunity to practise their specialised maternity skills, including delivery techniques. It is unwarranted, however, to conclude that all types of organisational employment tend to detract from professionalism.

What is suggested here is a refinement of the sociological literature that embraces the medicalisation thesis: some health critics have viewed the past, when lay midwives simply 'stood by' and patiently waited to 'catch the baby,' mainly in a positive light (Cartwright 1979, Oakley 1980; Haire 1972; Greer 1984; Rothman 1982). While such a tendency towards 'critical nostalgia' (Williams 1973:12) can be helpful in challenging the many negative aspects of medically-dominated maternity care, the accompanying bias towards premodern midwifery remains problematic.

Genuine professionalism was an elusive goal for traditional Newfoundland and Labrador granny midwives. The grannies' detailed narratives of midwifery practice in the isolated outport communities of premodern Newfoundland and Labrador paint a quite different picture than most of the recent academic accounts of traditional lay midwifery. At least in this particular historical instance, solo practice in clients' homes did not result in genuine worker control. For the granny midwives were 'independent' only in the narrow sense that they worked alone, without access to a bona fide division of labour. In reality, they had little autonomy as traditional homebirth attendants, not least because they were forced to travel long distances in all kinds of weather to their dispersed sites of practice; but they also lacked crucial materials (fresh bedsheets, diapers, etc.), and they had to perform numerous housekeeping tasks—cooking meals, washing soiled clothes, cleaning up after the entire household—in exchange for perhaps a dozen cabbage, a brace of rabbits or a few pounds of saltfish. Even their counterparts in small-scale clinics and nursing stations did not fare much better. Although enjoying a government salary, they nevertheless remained bound to a debilitating 24-hour schedule and were forced to 'make do' without recourse to either support staff, medical specialists, life-saving technology or collegial contact. By contrast, midwives in the cottage hospitals, while also on government salary, were able to practise as midwifery *specialists*, savouring a level of autonomy unknown to their forerunners in both home and clinics.

A graduating class of midwives from the Midwives Club, St. John's, Newfoundland, 1924.

Photo. Halloway. Courtesy of *The Newfoundland Quarterly*, Autumn, 1924; Harry Cuff Publications Ltd.

Although a larger section of today's homebirth clients experience a comparatively high standard of living and access to more efficient means of transportation and communication than their premodern counterparts, and although there is ready access to portable birthing equipment (including oxygen), genuine professionalism for present-day lay midwives in homebirth practice in the Netherlands also remains evasive. Not only do they have to contend with many of the problems associated with traditional midwifery (24-hour call, precarious remuneration, lack of collegial support and the absence of a career ladder), but today's homebirth midwives in the Netherlands, for example, face persistent obstacles that were largely absent from the work world of their traditional counterparts, not least intense competition from community physicians, falling birth rates and improved methods of monitoring and surveillance by their homebirth clientele (via the use, for example, of beepers). Many of these obstacles to professionalism for present-day lay midwives in the Netherlands have recently been documented among homebirth practitioners in the United States as well (Weitz & Sullivan 1985).[1] The goal of professionalism has been approximated to a far greater extent by present-day Swedish midwives and their Newfoundland and Labrador counterparts in small organizations.

Recent nostalgia for a vanished style of informal apprenticeship training must be called into question as well. Even grannies genuinely attracted to maternity work at an early age point to numerous problems besetting this mode of preparation. The apprenticeship system aimed at perfecting a 'hands-on' healing art based on practical knowledge derived from watching other village midwives, from personal experience, and from performing many deliveries. This common-sense approach was governed by guidelines set down by tradition rather than by rational science. While it gained some midwives a certain local charisma as 'wise women,' it failed to gain them a reputation for *expertise*. Although apprenticeship-trained midwives were effective in caring for normal maternity cases, their limited obstetric knowledge and life-saving skills, and lack of access to even rudimentary technology and medical services frequently left them unable to deal with emergencies. Moreover, the perpetual shortage of local recruits forced many novices into solo practice long before they were fully prepared. These difficult conditions of apprenticeship training often tempered a granny's initial commitment to the service of pregnant women in her community. Although there are without doubt differences between the apprenticeship training of today's lay midwives and that of the Newfoundland and Labrador granny midwives of the past (DeVries

1985), a word of caution is in order regarding the suitability of this style of preparing midwives for maternity work. At the very least, close examination of existing apprenticeship programs should be carried out in order to critically assess their adequacy.

Data on midwifery in Sweden and my own findings on Newfoundland and Labrador do not support the view (Derber 1982; Sorenson & Sorenson 1974; Larson 1977; Ritzer & Walczak 1988) that non-elite health service occupations in organisational employment have increasingly become deprofessionalised as a result of the actions of physicians practising professional dominance and administrators implementing bureaucratic controls. Also significant, according to writers embracing this deprofessionalisation thesis, has been the encroachment of advanced technology on workers' traditional mandates of practice, forcing them to manipulate machines that block rather than foster communication with clients (Johnson 1972; Haug 1975; 1983). In addition, it is asserted that the academisation of service occupations has reinforced this deprofessionalisation process, making service workers mere 'technocrats' and 'machine-minders,' well versed in the *science* of their occupation but lacking knowledge in the *art* of practice (Illich 1971; Toren 1975).

Both proponents of the medicalisation thesis and advocates of the deprofessionalisation approach have sometimes tended towards a certain nostalgia in their view of traditional craft training and practice. Newfoundland and Labrador granny midwives, by contrast, have been swift to distance themselves from any depiction of their occupation that equates professionalism with solo practice and apprenticeship training. In their shared judgment, such a view of the past captures only the pleasant side of an occupational culture that was recurrently characterised by serious hardships.

My data on Newfoundland and Labrador midwifery also raise questions about the 'professionalisation thesis' of occupational development. The view that large complex organisations *enhance* professionalism (Bell 1976) may help us understand the situation of top professionals located at the apex of the occupational hierarchy, but the situation of the majority of service workers in bureaucratic organisations continues to elude us. Rather than becoming a 'new class' (Gouldner 1978) or 'knowledge elite' (Bell 1980) with hitherto unknown 'professional powers' (Freidson 1986), the fate of my midwifery respondents in today's high-tech hospitals is a bleak one in comparison to the relatively high professional status formerly enjoyed by their colleagues in cottage hospitals.

Contrary to the prediction by advocates of the professionalisation thesis that university education will magnify opportunities for the achievement of professional status, the midwives in my sample have failed to achieve this. Academic graduates, undoubtedly well versed in the 'science' of midwifery, may be expert 'assessors' of the mental status of their clients. But they score poorly on the acquisition of both practical skills and socio-cultural awareness of their clients, in part because they are under the continuous supervision of medical specialists and hospital administrators during a substantial part of their clinical training in large bureaucratic hospitals—a situation which persists once they have entered the world of work.

In short, changes in the location and scale of workplace, intricacy of the division of labour and level of technological resources have together significantly transformed the configuration of the midwifery occupation in Newfoundland and Labrador in the 20th century.[2] Only during the historical period from the mid-1930s to mid-1960s—the heyday of the cottage hospitals, marked by moderate socio-economic development and pivotal welfare state reforms—did midwives savour a measure of professionalism in both their occupational preparation and work. This was made possible by the cottage hospitals' small yet efficient midwifery-staffed maternity wards. Medical practitioners and technology were available in case of obstetrical problems, but remained marginal to the care of women experiencing normal deliveries. At the same time, support personnel, by relieving cottage hospital midwives of maintenance and clean-up duties, provided them opportunities to specialise in maternity work and to socialise new recruits along a similar path. Finally, since cottage hospital midwives were preferred over their general nursing counterparts in promotion to managerial positions, substantial occupational mobility was possible on the maternity ward itself.

Only cottage hospital midwives—trained in a vocational program of study—were effective in balancing the theoretical and practical knowledge contents of their occupation. Like both their clinic and bureaucratic counterparts, cottage hospital midwives were schooled in the science of midwifery. Yet they were uniquely advantaged in that they also received counsel in the art of maternity care, gained from extensive practical experience in their unassuming yet adequate workplace. This distinctive training ground allowed neophytes in vocational training to relate midwifery theory to practice, to 'learn while doing.' Moreover, the cottage hospitals made provision for their vocationally-trained midwives to keep newly acquired skills, including expertise in conducting deliveries, honed. Since these midwives practised at a time when the birth rate was high, in work sites where medical presence was low, and prior to the emergence of outside competition for clients from large bureaucratic hospitals, they had access to a large pool of pregnant women. This nicely stabilised situation encountered by vocationally-trained graduates in the cottage hospitals—adequate client supply without overload—created an atmosphere conducive to frequent and sympathetic interaction with expectant mothers. The cottage hospital midwives drew upon their personal acquaintances with clients, carried them through their entire reproductive cycle, and often attended their subsequent pregnancies and those of female kin as well. In sum, vocationally-trained midwives in the cottage hospitals were genuine professionals, able to utilise their specialised knowledge in daily practice. Genuine professionalism was as unattainable for traditional apprentice-trained lay midwives in solo practice and for their counterparts in clinics outside an organised division of labour as for modern-day university-educated midwives in large hospital settings overshadowed by medical specialists and advanced technology. Exploration of the comparable situation of lay and clinic midwives elsewhere, as well as of other categories of independent practitioners, is needed in order to test the generalisability of my research findings in this regard. Moreover, studies of service employees in both small and large workplaces, akin to the cottage hospitals of the former era and present-day bureaucratic work sites, might test my own finding of the significance of organisational scale in the achievement of professionalism.

What is suggested by these results is a more 'grounded' approach (Glaser & Strauss 1967) to the changing situation of service workers. Such an open perspective allows us to unearth unanticipated data, including the possibility that occupational development in the health field may, in fact, not follow a linear path toward medicalisation and deprofessionalisation, on the one hand, or professionalisation, on the other, but that instead the transformation of many health service occupations may be receptive to 'negotiation' during crucial periods (Hall 1946, 1949; Strauss 1978). An empirically-based approach that pays attention to the potential *heterogeneity* concealed behind such abstract categories as patriarchy, bureaucracy and technocracy is critical to our understanding of the actual circumstances of occupational groups (Bendix 1984; Abbott 1988; Clifford and Marcus 1986). The modernisation of traditional service occupations in the West has not been a seamless web. On the contrary, as I have argued throughout this book, alternative developmental paths have emerged across and even within geo-political boundaries. Newfoundland and Labrador mid-wifery, for example, has not advanced along a straight evolutionary course from traditional lay practice in clients' homes to present-day employment in large complex organisations. Rather, in this particular historical instance, the transition pattern has been both more complicated and divergent, creating along the way a unique institution—the cottage hospital—in which professional midwifery succeeded. Of course, this period of cottage hospital midwifery was, except in northern areas, relatively short-lived; nevertheless, knowledge of its inner workings, from the perspectives of the participants themselves, at least indicates that existing paradigms of service work are in no way cast in stone.

In brief, a comparative-historical approach can provide many of the conceptual tools for interpreting research data on service occupations akin to Newfoundland and Labrador midwifery. While calling into question the widespread notion of a 'golden age' of service work located either in the past, outside a circumscribed division of labour, or within a highly complex one in the present, such an approach reveals instead a measure of professionalism secured in modest work sites.

POLICY IMPLICATIONS

Is there a message here regarding the type of occupational preparation and work structure most suitable for both midwives and clients? Before addressing this question, a cautionary note is in order: my data suggest that we must proceed judiciously, basing our recommendations for change on solid evidence. The recent tendency among social critics to reminisce about the 'good old days' of independent service work must be avoided. As the grannies and clinic midwives in my study have been quick to point out, the difficulties of 'independent' practice in the past far outweighed any social prestige they achieved during their careers. Macintyre (1977:22) lends support to this realist position:

> [M]y comparisons between anthropological accounts of childbirth in primitive societies and the criticisms directed towards modern obstetric practices have...led me to develop a skepticism about the primitive ('nice') versus modern ('nasty') distinction that underlies many of these recent critiques of modern obstetrics. I am not arguing that there is nothing wrong with modern obstetric practices...What I would argue is that the use of imaginative reconstructions of 'natural' childbirth in primitive societies as a standard against which to measure modern techniques may be factually incorrect and even counter-productive.

To regard notions of a past pristine epoch of midwifery as counterproductive does not mean, however, that developing countries should import Western models of scientific obstetrics and high-technology en masse and dismiss indigenous methods of recruitment and education as antiquated and worthless. Not only would such a direction for change be exceedingly costly—in fact, out of reach for most Third World societies—but, judging from present-day dissatisfaction of many North American and British women with modern bureaucratic obstetrics and its iatrogenic complications, such a rapid developmental path may in the long term prove regressive, creating a whole new set of problems for women in developing countries, although of a very different nature than those associated with traditional lay healing practices.[3] Is there a middle route between these two polar systems of maternity care—independent and bureaucratic—which can balance the advantages of each while avoiding their shortcomings?

One way forward may lie in the adoption of a more pragmatic (and less extravagant) reform strategy, which takes into account the needs of both midwives and clients in their particular socio-cultural locations. My own findings highlight the crucial importance of *workplace* in bringing about this desired goal. Neither home, clinic, nor bureaucracy emerged as ideal grounds for Newfoundland and Labrador midwives' occupational preparation and practice. Only in the cottage hospitals, arranged around a midwifery rather than a medical model, thereby making available a 'homey' atmosphere pleasing to clients while granting its staff a measure of freedom from debilitating community control, did midwives reach a level of professionalism coveted by all; only in these small organisations were they provided ample opportunity to keep their newly acquired skills sharpened, while at the same time enjoying access to a safety net of medical expertise and technology in case of abnormality.

In brief, institutionalisation of a cottage type hospital system in both cities and towns, in amalgamation with a vocational education plan for preparing maternity attendants—similar to the current Swedish system of training and practice—would be relatively inexpensive to implement and might go a long way toward meeting many of the concerns of both indigenous midwives and pregnant women in developing countries. Native-born midwives would thereby be able to up-grade their lay skills—at least initially this would have to involve the help of vocational teachers from either within the country or from abroad—while continuing to practise in small maternity hospitals in the vicinity of their home communities. Social welfare benefits, including, in addition to maternity care, safe birth control and abortion, free of charge and universal, would no doubt enormously increase the likelihood that such a midway proposal for change could eventually meet its avowed goal of balancing the benefits accrued by practitioners and clients. Competent and committed indigenous and immigrant midwives, with knowledge of the latest birth control methods and abortion techniques and access to the necessary facilities, could help make childbirth a real *choice* rather than the destiny of the women under their care. Of course, unless accompanied by increased educational and employment opportunities for women in the developing world, such reproductive reforms would still have only limited impact.

And what about midwives and pregnant women closer to home? As is the case for their counterparts in Third World societies, a great deal depends upon background characteristics of the clients themselves. This holds especially true in the United States, where a fragmentary maternity-care system based on a corporate model has resulted in sharp inequalities of access to specialists, hospitals and medical technology. But even in Britain and Canada, large groups of birthing women have in recent decades been marginalised or silenced into submission by the medical specialists and bureaucrats dominating the organisation of maternity care. The policy recommendations mentioned above—a midwifery-staffed cottage hospital system (or mothercare or free-standing birthing centres) accompanied by vocational instruction for midwives—may also help improve the health status and comfort of pregnant women belonging to racial and ethnic minorities as well as those who are poor and reside inside or outside large metropolitan areas. Preliminary analysis of my ongoing research on clients' perspectives of cottage hospital midwifery in present-day northern areas (still considered by health authorities to be 'peripherally located' and thus an acceptable place for midwives to practise!) indicates that the vast majority of pregnant women there—with the exception of a small female elite who tend to deliver in a large bureaucratic hospital under the care of a high-tech obstetrical team—strongly support midwives over doctors and delivery in cottage hospitals over either the home, clinic or large bureaucracy.[4] Perhaps less-advantaged groups of women elsewhere in North America and Britain might also enjoy recourse to such an alternative maternity-care arrangement, as well as an extension of the limited birth control and abortion services now at their disposal.

The question persists whether more privileged clients would opt for a similar style of midwifery preparation and work structure. As feminists have pointed out concerning current British and North

American ways of birth (Oakley 1984; Eakins 1986; Jordan 1983), *medical safety* remains a fundamental concern among women of the upper strata, most of whom, seemingly inattentive to expense, expect access to high-powered specialists and the latest obstetrical techniques in order to 'guarantee' a perfect baby (an elusive dream since no amount of preplanning can actually insure a successful pregnancy outcome). But in other historical periods and in certain regions of present-day Western society even today, the concern with medical risk has not altogether eliminated other considerations. Such was the case until recently in Newfoundland, where safety and the psycho-social well-being of birthing clients were given equal attention. To some extent this is still the case now. And a similar situation exists in Sweden concerning the highly personal experience of the reproductive passage, which, in the shared judgment of Swedish women of different geographic locations and social class backgrounds, is best achieved by way of vocationally-trained midwives in small mothercare centres (Jordan 1983).

In a very real sense, future modifications in the existing patterns of childbirth, in both developing and developed countries, depend upon the changing position of women — as service workers and clients across and within national boundaries.

Appendix I: Interview Schedule

My research project, which aimed at obtaining detailed descriptions by the midwives themselves of the occupation of midwifery and the organisation of maternity care in their specific socio-cultural location and historical period, required a relatively open-ended questionnaire—essentially, a series of queries or probes to help navigate the exchange. While many respondents offered additional data, all of them contributed information on the following general areas of inquiry:

1. Personal biographical details: Date and place of birth? Mother's /father's/husband's occupation? Informal/formal education? Certificates, degrees? Marital status? Number of children? Personal birth stories?

2. Decision to undertake the role of midwife: Experienced a special 'calling' to this line of work? Passed down by oral tradition from female relatives? Appointed by the local community to the 'office' of midwife? Due to circumstance—no one else available?

3. Type of Schooling and Socialisation: Informal apprenticeship? Vocational preparation? Academic education? Extent of community and practical experience? Type and level of socio-cultural knowledge of clients?

4. Access to specialised knowledge: Main sources of information concerning female reproductive care—Observation only? Oral tradition? Midwifery teachers? Other health professionals, such as nurses and doctors? Popular books? Medical texts?

5. Philosophy on birth: View of women's reproductive passage: Natural event? Medical procedure? Private choice? Perspective on birth control and abortion?

6. Work structure:
    1) Site of practice: Home? Clinic/nursing station? Cottage hospital? Regional/referral hospital?
    2) Circumstances of workplace—Geographical location? Physical plant? Available resources? Occupational hierarchy? Level of technology? Recourse to colleagues? Time schedule? Pace of practice? Fringe benefits? Holidays? Vacation pay? Pregnancy leaves?
    3) Level of work specialisation: General nursing duties? Maintenance tasks? Maternity assignments?
7. Payment for services rendered: Without remuneration? Sliding scale, depending on circumstances of clients? Barter system of exchange? Formal fee-for-service? Government salary?
8. Control/discipline of work activities: Informal client/community guidelines? Formal rules and regulations established in the Midwives' Act? Role of significant others: Family/community leaders? Midwifery supervisors? Medical personnel? Hospital administrators? Government authorities? Reasons for chastisement and/or dismissal?
9. Role as a midwifery teacher: Informal? Formal? Biographical descriptions of students?
10. Life situations of clients: Socio-economic circumstances? Work roles? Family roles? Quality of relationship with fathers, husbands and male clergy and physicians? Level of reproductive choice?
11. Role in the community: Wise woman? Professional midwife? Rank-and-file worker?
12. Disruptions in career path: Due to: Further education? Motherhood? Ill-health? Burnout? Old age?
13. Future perspective on midwifery: Policy recommendations regarding midwifery and maternity care in the province? In Canada as a whole? In global view?

Appendix II: Midwives' Manual

Source: Newfoundland Department of Health

I attended   Mrs _____

            Address _____

on_____
    DAY/MONTH/YEAR

    She was in labour _____hrs.

    The water broke at _____ time

    The baby was born at _____ time

    Head first_____   Feet first _____

The after-birth came _____ time

    She had (a lot of bleeding) _____
            (very little bleeding)_____
            (moderate bleeding) _____

Was the patient seen by a Doctor or District Nurse before the baby was born?

Was the woman torn?

    (a) small tear   _____
    (b) medium tear   _____
    (c) large tear   _____

Was Doctor notified? _____

What was the weight of the baby? _____

Did you put silver nitrate in the eyes? _____

Was the baby a boy or a girl? _____

Did you put the baby to the breast in 6 hours to nurse? _____

If not, why not? _____

Did you tell the woman to nurse the baby every 3 hours? _____

    If not, why not? _____

Is the baby's foreskin tight? _____

Did you push it back? _____

Did you tell the baby's mother to keep it clean under the
foreskin? _____

Are the mother's nipples sore? _____

Did you advise her to wash them with boiled water before
nursing baby? _____

Did the mother suffer from afterpains? _____

Did you give her Liquid Extract of Ergot? _____

How much Ergot did you give her? _____

**This declaration is made and signed by me and to the best of my
knowledge and belief is true.**

MIDWIFE   _____

ADDRESS   _____

DATE_____19_____

MIDWIFERY SAFETY RULES

1. A midwife, before attending a woman in confinement, must wash her hands and arms well with warm water and soap; and afterwards, wash in a quart of warm water containing a teaspoonful of lysol, or carbolic acid, or other antiseptic. Use a brush.

2. She must keep herself clean, and also her patient, bed, clothing and all that comes in contact with her.

3. She must not pass her fingers or any instrument into the birth canal of the woman, for the purpose of making an examination or for any other purpose.

4. A midwife must endeavour to secure the assistance of a doctor if the child is not born after eighteen hours of labour.

5. A midwife is not permitted to give drugs of any kind to hasten labour pains, but may give castor oil or other laxative as needed.

6. She must not give an injection of any kind into the birth canal without orders from a doctor, but may use an enema of warm water into the bowels to produce a bowel movement.

7. If the child's hand comes down, the child is lying in a cross position and cannot be born alone. Try to get a doctor at once, telling him what you have noticed.

8. If the child's feet or buttocks are born first, it will be smothered in a few minutes unless the head comes out immediately. In such a case, the midwife should lift the body of the child by the feet and hold it up. This will make the delivery of the head quicker. Delay will almost certainly mean the death of the child.

9. If the mother has a spasm, or bleeds either before or after the child is born, send at once for a doctor, if one is within reach. Do the same thing if the mother is very weak or her labour is slow. If the mother shows signs of fever, try to reach a doctor at once, and do not wait until she is worse. Unless treated promptly, she may die. Do not rely upon yourself if there is anything unusual about the case—send for the doctor as quickly as you can.

10. Every midwife in the country must report the births she attends within ten days on the report forms given her. In the cities, midwives are required to report sooner. Use unfading black ink (writing fluid).

11. If the cord comes down, the foot of the bed should be raised and a doctor called at once.

12. Blindness from birth is due to inflammation of the eyes. This may be caused by germs of disease from the birth canal or the bowel movements of the mother. The Department of Health provides registered and licensed midwives with a solution to use on the eyes of newborn babies and to prevent permanent injury to the sight. Two drops of this solution are put into each eye of the infant as soon as the child is born. Do not ask the mother if you may use the drops. In the interest of the child you must do so. Separate the eyelids gently before making the application. A little redness of the eyes may be noticed for a day or two after but this is nothing to be worried about.

Midwives who want any further information as to the Rules and Regulations stated above or wanting special instruction about anything should write their inquiries to the Supervisor of Midwives for their own district, or where no such official has been appointed, to the Dept. of Health, St. John's Newfoundland.

FAILURE TO DO ANY OF THESE MAKES YOU LIABLE TO THE LAW, AND TO LOSE YOUR PERMIT EVEN AFTER IT HAS BEEN GIVEN YOU.

PRENATAL CARE

Prenatal care is the care and supervision given to a pregnant woman so that she may pass through the dangers of pregnancy with the maximum of mental and physical fitness at its termination, with the reward of a well baby and with the knowledge whereby mother and baby may be kept well.

The maternity service includes care and supervision during the complete maternal cycle—before the baby is born, at delivery and for the next six weeks.

1. DIET

Instructions on good food during pregnancy are at the end of the folder.

2. REST AND EXERCISE

The pregnant woman should have at least eight hours sleep at night in a well aired room and rest periods during the day. Household duties may be carried on and regular exercise should be taken in the out of doors if possible. She should not move heavy furniture or carry heavy buckets of water uphill. She should walk in the open air every day if possible. She should be especially careful not to over exert herself at the time her monthly periods would ordinarily appear. Deep breathing exercises are beneficial.

3. CLOTHING

This should be light and loose fitting with weight hanging from the shoulders. A stomach binder made to support the stomach may be worn if a maternity girdle is unobtainable or too expensive for the patient. The stockings should be kept up with suspenders fastened to girdle. Round elastic garters interfere with blood circulation and should not be worn.

Shoes should have low broad heels.

4. CARE OF SKIN

A daily warm bath is advised but after the seventh month this should not be taken in a tub. It is most important that the body should be kept clean.

5. CARE OF TEETH

The teeth should be cleaned at least twice a day. A solution of baking soda or salt may be used as a mouth wash.

6. CARE OF BREASTS

Special care should be given the breasts and nipples after the seventh month. Use absorbent cotton in cleansing the nipples with warm water and soap. Dry carefully. A little vaseline could be applied after giving this care. Before giving care the hands should be carefully washed.

7. SIGNS OF LABOUR

Labour begins with pains in the back and abdomen, and a watery discharge which may be blood tinged. Note when the pains begin and how often they occur. While waiting, boil a large quantity of water in a covered vessel and set aside to cool. Prepare delivery bed. Place conveniently the supplies needed for mother and baby.

NEEDED SUPPLIES

MOTHER'S LIST

Clean sheets and blankets
Pillow Cases
Towels and Wash Cloths
Two Nightgowns
2 binders (of old linen or unbleached cotton)
2 large confinement newspaper pads
    (made as shown during midwifery course at clinic.)
4 similar pads, in smaller size (as shown)
Material for sanitary pads
Safety pins
4 wooden blocks for bed when it is a low one
Bed Pan
1 jar with cover (for sterile water)
2 basins - medium size
1 small bowl or jug with cover
1 hand brush
Plenty of clean newspapers or oilcloth or rubber sheet to
protect bed.
    (Have patient collect and save pieces of old household
    linen, wash, boil, dry in the sun and iron with a hot iron.
    Those may be kept in a clean pillow case and will be
    found useful at the time of confinement.)

Breast Tray
    Jar with cover for sterile water
    Covered jar for swabs
    Paper bag

Tray for Perineal Care
    Large jar with cover for sterile water
    Sterile Jug
    Vulva pads (sterile)
    Paper bag
    Absorbent squares (sterile)

DIRECTIONS FOR MAKING AND STERILIZING SUPPLIES

Before making supplies the hands should be carefully scrubbed with special
attention to cleanliness of finger nails. A clean dress or apron should be
worn and there should be a clean surface on which to work. Clean supplies
should be used. Supplies should be ready by the end of the seventh month.
A small supply should be sterilized for emergency use and the remainder
put away in a clean pillow case to be sterilized shortly before confinement
is expected.

Material needed:

> 2 rolls of Absorbent Cotton
> 10 yds. Gauze
> > (failing this, old clean linen may be used)

How to cut material:

> (1) Absorbent Cotton

Cut 50 strips, 4 inches wide across the rolls of absorbent. From each of the 50 strips cut off squares of about 4 inches. These may be used to cleanse vaginal parts during the delivery, and if any left over to wash nipples before baby is taken to nurse.

> (2) Gauze

Cut the gauze to cover the 50 pads into pieces 18 x 12 inches.

How to wrap supplies:

Wrap pads in bundles of three for sterilization in unbleached cotton or pieces of old sheeting being careful to have all of the contents of the bundle covered, and pin or sew the wrapping securely. Make one bundle of twenty absorbent cotton squares for use at confinement, and ten bundles of six for use in daily postpartum care and wrap the same as the pads.

How to Sterilize Supplies:

Bake bundles in an oven at 350 degrees F. for one hour (this is quite a hot oven, the degree of heat being slightly less than that used for baking bread). For the first half hour a pan of water should be placed in the oven to prevent scorching, then it should be removed in order that the bundles will be thoroughly dry at the end of an hour. At the end of the hour's baking the wrappings should be a light brown or tan colour. The sterilized bundles should be put in a clean pillow case in a drawer until needed.

Layette for the Baby

> 3 flannelette nightgowns, open down back
> 3 shirts, buttoning down front, long sleeves, wool and silk or wool and cotton mixture.
> 3 bands, 6 inches wide, and 18-22 inches long of fine white flannel or flannelette, edges not hemmed or bound. When the cord has healed these bands are no longer necessary.
> 2 dozen (at least) 24 inches square of soft flannelette for diapers
> A shawl or baby blanket
> 2 baby blankets for bed
> 4 to 6 sheets
> 2 rubber sheets or squares of oil cloth of plastic to protect the mattress.

Baby's Tray:

    Covered jar of cold boiled water for cleansing nipples
    Covered jar for absorbent cotton swabs
    Covered jar for clean nipples
    Covered jar for soiled nipples
    Bottle of boiled water with cork (baby's supply of drinking water)
    Nursing bottle
    Covered dish for olive oil
    Covered dish for bath soap
    Safety pins in cake of soap
    Paper bag.

Baby's Bed

It is very important that the new baby should sleep alone. A large basket or a bureau drawer could make a suitable and inexpensive bed. If a basket is used it should be lined with a washable material to protect the baby from draughts. The mattress should be firm and soft and may be made from several folds of woollen blanket.

THE MIDWIFE MAY CARRY OUT THE FOLLOWING PRENATAL EXAMINATION

1. Palpitation of the abdomen as done at the prenatal clinic during the two months training in St. John's.

2. Some of the conditions which would lead one to suspect an abnormal pelvis are:

        Bandy legs
        Hump Back
        Narrowness across the hips
        History of previous difficult confinements.

3. Examination of Urine

The midwife should watch for certain danger signals, and if these symptoms occur should seek advice from the nearest doctor or nurse or write the Supervisor of Midwives, at St. John's

The symptoms to be watched for are:

    1. Vaginal bleeding, no matter how slight

    2. Swelling of the face or fingers

    3. Severe continuous headache

    4. Dimness or blurring of vision

    5. Pain in the abdomen

    6. Persistent vomiting

    7. Chills and Fever

    8. Sudden escape of fluid from the vagina

PREPARATION FOR DELIVERY

Remove all unnecessary furniture from the room. The tables left should be conveniently placed for working. Make sure that there is good lighting. If the bed is low there should be blocks to raise it up. Have ready a clean supply of linen and plenty of hot and cold boiled water in covered containers.

A supply of old newspapers should be on hand for protecting surfaces and also for waste bags. A pail for waste water is also necessary. Protect the surfaces of tables with thick pads of newspaper and clean towels.

Place on the Tables the following:-

1. Container in which the following are sterilized. Teaspoon, scissors, artery forceps, rubber catheters.

2. Sterile Perineal pads

3. Vaseline

4. Binder

5. Safety pins

6. Clean towels

7. Sterile basin to place in position for placenta

8. Silver Nitrate for baby's eyes

9. Sterile cord ties and dressing

10. Small bowl of hot water in which jar of olive oil has been placed.

11. Scales

12. Sterile basin for hands with soap and clean towel.

Wear a clean-freshly laundered gown. Place sterile articles on one table and the other articles on a second table or bureau.

PREPARE BABY'S BED - by lining a blanket with a diaper to receive the baby. Arrange clothing as each garment will be required and wrap around hot water bottle.

PREPARATION OF MOTHER AND BED - Put on a tight bottom sheet. Place over this two large newspaper pads covered with clean linen. Place a small newspaper pad at foot of bed on which to place baby.

Put the patient to bed, shave pubic area, scrub hands and cleanse area well. Apply sterile perineal pad. Instruct patient not to use toilet but bedpan, especially if the waters have broken or if there is any bloody discharge.

First Care of Baby

After the baby is born and cord cut and tied, apply sterile dressing and wrap in clean warm covering until the mother is cared for. Put baby on side, head lower than feet to allow mucus to escape.

Care of Mother

When the after-birth has come and the womb is firm, wash off with sterile water between the legs and hips. Put on two sterile pads and a binder.

Remove from bed all soiled papers, pads or sheets. After washing patient's face and hands finish making bed.
Examine after-birth carefully, to see that it is all there, then make sure that it is burned.

To Prevent Bleeding

Five one teaspoonful Fluid Extract Ergot after the delivery of the after-birth and repeat dose in four hours. This also helps to check after pains.

Further Care of Baby

Examine cord. Re-tie if necessary, look for bleeding from the cord, then apply sterile dressing. Put drops in eyes (solution of silver nitrate 1% in wax capsules.) Pierce the end of the capsule with coarse needle. Press the capsule between your thumb and finger and you will readily get a drop for one eye, press again and you will get another drop for the second eye. Oil the baby, and put on smooth binder—weigh. Continue dressing, then put in warm bed already prepared. Advise the mother when to feed.

Care of Premature Infant

The infant should be handled as little as possible, and when it is necessary, on a pillow. All care except breast feeding should be given within the basket. An incubator should be made from a good sized flat bottomed basket, or a crib lined with a sheet. An enveloping blanket should be placed under a pillow or mattress which is protected with a rubber sheet or newspaper pad and a quilted pad. Fasten three hot water bottles to the sides and foot of the basket. Great care should be taken to prevent burning. The temperature of the incubator should be 80 degrees to 90 degrees F. Warm oil should be used for bathing. Dress in band, diaper and shirt and premature jacket made from cotton wool. Also wrap in a soft blanket. The feeding should be done carefully and regularly. Breast feeding every three hours. The breast milk may have to be drawn out with a breast pump if the baby is too weak to nurse. It is then fed to the baby, warm, with a medicine dropper.

DAILY CARE OF MOTHER AND BABY

Make sure that there is plenty of hot water for bathing and boiled hot and cold water for special care of the mother. Keep these covered until ready to use. See that room is warm. Prepare basin for washing, on table or chair near bed. Wash hands and put on apron or smock. Take temperature.

Place paper on floor to put soiled clothes on. Have pail to put the baby's soiled diaper in. Keep baby's soiled clothes in a separate piece of paper.

Place near at hand:

1. Clean diaper for breasts
2. Binder
3. Bed linen (if being changed)
4. Fresh nightgown (if being changed)
5. Orange stick to clean fingernails (*on table*)
6. Milk soap (*on table*)
7. Packages of sterile sanitary pads and sterile swabs (*on table*)
8. Jug with hot boiled water. (Add cold boiled water to bring it to right temperature before using.) (*on table*)
9. Covered bowl with boiled water and a little mild soap. (A scald plate or saucer may be used as cover.) (*on table*)

Remove bed spread and blanket - place over chair to air. Place patient on bed pan. Have patient place soiled pad in paper bag then pin bag on side of bed near the foot. Note whether the discharge is normal. Note whether the womb feels firm. Remove binder. If it is to be worn again place on chair. Drape patient with sheet. Patient can help with this so that she will not be uncovered before it is necessary.

Special care for Mother

1. Wash own hands using orange stick for nails.
2. Open packages of sanitary pads and swabs.
3. Test water in jug to see if it is too hot by pouring a little over own wrist.
4. Pour some of it into scalded bowl which has a small piece of milk soap in it.
5. Wash own hands and arms thoroughly.
6. Wash between patients legs using sterile swabs and soapy water in bowl. Do not try to wash inside, then rinse off by pouring water from jug.
7. Use swabs only once then throw into paper bag.
8. Dry with fresh swabs and put on clean sanitary pad.
9. Finish by washing buttocks and dry thoroughly.
10. Remove bed pan and put a clean piece of sheeting under patient's buttocks. The bed should be protected by a rubber sheet, oil cloth or newspaper under the small sheet.
11. Wash hands again.
12. Close up packages of sanitary pads and swabs for the next time special care is needed. Leave a package of sanitary pads near the patient and a clean paper bag so that she can change them when necessary.
13. Scald bowl and cover.

14. Scald three jars and fill with boiled water, ready for the mother's care, her breasts and for baby's drinking water.

15. Remove paper bag with soiled pads and burn.

Bed Bath

Wash hands then

1. Put fresh hot water in basin.

2. Place blanket over patient – remove nightgown.

3. Place towel under head and one across top of blanket.

4. Wash face, neck and ears – dry. Then wash arms. Pay special attention to underarms. Let patient wash own hands.

5. Change water and use fresh wash cloth – then wash breasts – dry and place clean diaper across the breasts.'

6. Wash stomach and then each leg and feet. Place a large towel under the leg as it is being washed. Only uncover the part being washed.

7. Have patient turn over and wash back with fresh water. Dry well.

8. Put on fresh nightgown and make up bed.

DAILY ROUTINE FOR BABY'S BATH

The baby's bath may be given on the nurses' knee or on a table. The place selected must be warm and free from draughts and if possible where the mother can watch. Have everything ready before starting bath.

1. Baby's clothes warmed and arranged in order needed.

2. Tray with baby's things – e.g. soap, pins, oil etc.

3. Bath rub containing water 100 degrees F. (This may be tested by elbow) a jug of warm water.

4. Two soft towels and soft washcloth.

5. Newspapers spread on floor to receive soiled garments.

If bath is to be given on the table the baby should be placed on a thick pad protected by a rubber sheet or several thicknesses of newspaper covered by a diaper or towel. The mother should be told that the baby must never be left alone on the table.

Wash hands and put on mask.

The procedure for the bath is the same whether on a table or on the knee. Care must be taken to keep the baby covered and to handle him as little as possible.

Have a towel or pad under the baby and one on top to dry baby. Remove the nightgown and place on a newspaper, or if to be worn again place on the back of the chair to air. Inspect mouth and eyes unless there is inflammation or a discharge. In that case use warm boiled water and absorbent cotton swabs. Bathe gently, wiping swabs from inner corner of eye to outer and using each swab only once. Cleanse each nostril with small twist of absorbent cotton moistened in water. Wash and dry face and ears. Soap baby's head, hold over basin, rinse well, dry thoroughly.

Do not use soap on baby's face.

Remove soiled diaper. Place on newspaper. Cleanse buttocks with absorbent cotton and olive oil. Take temperature if necessary. With baby still lying on back, remove shirt from one arm and chest on one side, using soap gently wash arm, and half of chest and back. Dry oil creases and put clean shirt on this arm, and half of body. Remove soiled shirt. Dry gently. Oil creases without using too much oil on the skin. Put shirt on, this may be turned up over baby's arms if necessary to keep them from disturbing the cord dressing. Remove band, cover cord dressing with clean absorbent. Do not change cord dressing unless it is soiled and in that case wash hands before doing dressing. Cleanse area with boiled water and put on a clean band. Fasten with small safety pins. Wash legs. Separate and clean between legs carefully or push back foreskin very gently, bathing parts underneath to remove any material which may cause irritation. If foreskin is tight gently push it back. Oil creases of legs.

Put on diaper. When cord is off and stump is healed give tub bath. Wash face and head as before. Soap limbs and body. After testing temperature of water, place baby in tub, for a brief period rinsing well then remove from tub and wrap in towel. Pat dry. Put on shirt and finish dressing, wrap in light covering. Remove soiled material and water. Wash hands, set up trays, etc., ready for next visit. Give necessary instructions in regard to care and feeding of patient to responsible member of the family and attend to ventilation of room.

CARE OF BREASTS WHEN NURSING THE BABY

Breasts should be carefully washed with warm water and soap with special attention to nipples. Apply a clean cotton square over each nipple and a loose binder to breasts. Before each feeding of the baby the nipples and surrounding area should be cleansed with swabs (separate swab for each nipple) and jar of boiled water provided for this purpose. This area should also be cleansed and dried with swabs again after feeding to prevent cracking of nipples.

GENERAL INFORMATION

Retained Placenta (after-birth)

Placenta in Uterus

If the after-birth is separated the cord lengthens, the womb rises above the level of umbilicus; it is moveable and can be moved easily from side to side; it becomes pear shaped. If pressure is made backwards on womb the cord does not go back when pressure is stopped.

Treatment for Retained Placenta

If placenta has left uterus and is retained.

1. Pass catheter if patient has not voided for some time.
2. Express by pushing backwards and downwards on womb when it is contracting.

Haemorrhage

Haemorrhage may occur before, during or after labour.
Before or during labour it should always be considered serious, the patient may be in great danger, even with the best of care. Medical advice should be sought immediately.

Post-partum haemorrhage comes on after the child is born and may occur before or after the after-birth comes away. The womb, instead of being hard and round fills with blood and becomes large and soft. The patient becomes weak and pale. Ask for medical help, and while waiting try and keep the patient perfectly quiet, apply pressure or massage over the womb to cause contraction, this may stop the haemorrhage even before the arrival of the doctor.

Puerperal Fever

The birth of a baby causes numerous small wounds and unless absolute cleanliness is practised it is quite possible that germs may enter and cause a wound infection which can become very serious.

These germs may enter through the hands or from discharges of the mouth and nose. Therefore the midwife must be extremely careful over her person and materials that are to come in contact with the entrance to the womb. Under no circumstances is she allowed to make an inside examination before the birth of the baby or during labour.

Observe the Following Rules:

1. Have all materials, that are to come in contact with the entrance to the birth canal, sterile.
2. Scrub arms, hands and nails every time you give care (don't touch anything but sterile material when giving care.)
3. Keep person, bed linen, room etc., scrupulously clean.
4. Wear a mask when at delivery and when giving post-partum care. If possible avoid taking cases when you have a cold or infected finger, or any other infection.

Care of Cracked Nipples

Sore or cracked nipples are the starting of breast abscess, which is a serious condition, and affects both mother and child. This is sometimes caused by germs from the hands of the midwife. These germs get into the sores or cracks on the nipples from hands, clothing etc., and then get into the blood stream. These germs increase until the breasts become inflamed and often form an abscess. The nipples should be kept from getting sore, or healed as quickly as possible if they do get sore. The proper care of the breasts during the prenatal stage is very important and often prevents cracking of the nipples.

The sores will quickly heal if the baby is nursed through a glass nipple shield, but remember that the shield must be boiled each time before use. Apply hot (but not hot enough to burn the patient) compresses for twenty minutes every four hours. Use vaseline or lanolin between compresses. If the inflammation does not improve in a day or two try to get help from a doctor.

Treatment of Turned in Nipples

If the nipples are sunken, they should be drawn out twice a day for a couple of weeks before the baby is born, by a gentle pulling motion, while the breasts are being cleansed as instructed in the first pages of this pamphlet.

Scanty Milk Supply

When the flow of milk is scant, it may be increased by having the mother take freely of liquids between meals such as milk or cocoa made from milk, milk soups, etc.

Teaching the Baby to Nurse

The newborn baby must often require to be taught how to nurse. The midwife should stay with the baby to see that she nurses five minutes only during the first feeding (eight hours after birth) and instruct the mother to feed her for only five minute periods every six hours the first day. These periods being gradually increased up to twenty minutes and by the third or fourth days after that, it should be nursed at four hour intervals until bedtime and once during the night if necessary. Every midwife should make it plain to the mother that there is no food as good for the baby as the mother's milk. If there is not enough mother's milk let the baby have all there is, and then to make up the rest of the feeding use evaporated tinned milk, with two parts of water to one of milk. About two level teaspoonfuls of sugar should be divided amongst the feedings during a day. Warm the feeding before giving to the baby. If cows milk is used it should be boiled for ten minutes before using. Make up with two parts milk and one of water, the opposite of the amounts used with tinned milk.

Deformed Women

A number of women are deformed from rickets which they had in childhood caused by lack of calcium in the diet.

The bones of the hips through which the child passes may be flat and the bony canal narrowed, so that the child's head cannot pass.

You should advise every woman who is deformed to have a doctor make a careful examination and measurement of her hip bones.

If he finds out in time that she is too narrow for a full-grown child to pass through, he may bring on labour ahead of time and save the life of both mother and child or he may advise her to go to hospital for her delivery.

Natural Labour

Natural labour, with the child in correct position and the mother in natural and healthy condition, is not dangerous if properly managed. The most frequent and natural position for the child to be born in is with the head first, and the crown of the head turned to the front of the mother with face backward. When the crown is turned towards the mother's back, the labour is likely to be slower and more difficult and often calls for the use of instruments. A midwife could not tell the position of the head even if she risked putting her finger inside and should, therefore, not wait over eighteen hours from the beginning of regular pains before sending for a doctor. Longer waiting causes the woman to become worn out and exhausted. Natural labour is usually over in from twelve to eighteen hours and after the first birth is often shorter than that.

Breach or Foot Presentation is when the child comes with the buttocks or feet first. This presentation is usually no more dangerous for the mother, but the child is apt to be stillborn if not properly handled. If the head of the child is not delivered quickly after the body is born, the cord is squeezed between the head of the child and the bones of the mother, and as the child cannot breathe, it soon dies.

Records show that the midwives lose too many babies in breech presentation. Some midwives know nothing about hastening the birth of the head after the body is born. Any midwife can help in such a case. With the mother lying on her back, simply catch the child by the feet with the right hand, and raise its body up. That will make the position of the head better, and will take the weight of the baby's body off the mother. At the same time place the left hand over the lower portion of the mother's stomach and squeeze the womb, which may be felt hard and round, with the head still partly inside of it. This will also help to force the head out more quickly.

Transverse or Cross Presentation is when the child is lying crosswise in the womb. As the labour progresses, the bag of water is apt to break and one of the child's hands show outside. When the midwife sees this, she should not lose a minute in letting a doctor know. She should send him word just what she has seen and he will know that he cannot lose any time in getting there. It will be necessary for him to put the patient asleep and to pass his hand inside, catch the feet and turn the child. No midwife is expected to try any such thing, nor must she pull on the hand, as it is impossible for her to deliver the child in that way. An ignorant midwife has been known to pull the child's arm off and cause the death of mother and child, instead of getting a doctor at once. A midwife may suspect a transverse presentation, even if the hand does not show, if the labour makes no progress and the shape of the mother seems to show that the child is lying across. Then she should try to get help.

Face or Brow Presentation occasionally occurs also, and usually requires the aid of a doctor. If the midwife follows the rules not to wait over eighteen hours, she will usually get a doctor in time, when she has a case of that sort.

Puerperal Eclampsia (Convulsion or Spasms)

Puerperal convulsion may come on before, during, or after labour. This is one of the most frightful conditions that a midwife is apt to face, and calls for the immediate services of a doctor. She can do little else then, but may be able to prevent the trouble by advising her patient to consult a doctor when dangerous symptoms arise before the time of labour. These symptoms are severe swelling of various parts of the body, severe headache, pain below the breast bone, and bad eyesight. By the time the eyes become affected, the patient is in a bad condition and too much time is already lost. The trouble causing convulsions shows itself early in the kidneys, and for this reason careful doctors advise all of their patients to send them a bottle of urine to be tested, every two or four weeks, and oftener if there are any bad symptoms. Midwives should urge their patients who are doing badly to send the doctor a bottle of urine, and have him see them also. Three or four pints of urine should be passed in twenty four hours.

RULES WHICH EVERY MIDWIFE MUST OBSERVE

1. She must secure a midwife permit.
2. She must report every birth before ten days in the city (by cards obtained at the Post Office) and as soon as mail permits, in outports (by the report form provided for this purpose.)
3. She must not pass her fingers or any instrument or give an injection into the birth canal of her patient, and she must obey the other sanitary rules on the back of the application form.

QUESTIONS AND ANSWERS ON MIDWIFE WORK

LESSON I

1. What is the purpose of these classes?

Answer: The purpose of these classes is to learn the best way to take care of mothers and babies so that we may save their lives, and have well and strong mothers and babies instead of sick ones. To learn what a responsibility it is for an untrained midwife to have the lives of mothers and babies in her hands.

2.   What are the rules that every midwife must observe?

Answer: The rules that every midwife must observe are:

  a. She must secure a Midwife permit.

  b. She must report every birth before ten days.

  c. She must not pass her fingers or any instrument or give an injection into the birth canal of her patient, and

  d. she must obey the other sanitary rules on the back of her Permit, and application form.

3.   Why should a midwife not make inside examination?

Answer: A Midwife should not make inside examination because she may carry infection to the mother. Furthermore, she learns nothing from such an examination.

4.   What do the safety rules say about keeping clean?

Answer: The safety rules say that she must keep herself, her patient, her patient's bed, her patient's clothing and everything that touches her patient, clean.

5.   Do the safety rules permit a midwife to give drugs?

Answer: The safety rules say a midwife should never give any drugs to hasten or increase labour pains. She may give a laxative, such as castor oil, when needed for the bowels.

LESSON II

1.   When does the baby's life begin?

Answer: The baby's life begins nine months before it is born.

2.   How can we be sure that the baby is having good care all this time?

Answer: We can be sure the baby is having good care all this time by being sure that the mother has good care before the baby is born. We call this prenatal care. To receive prenatal care the mother must call us early in her pregnancy.

3.   How do we know when kidneys are not doing their work?

Answer: We know the kidneys are not doing their work when mother passes less than one quart of urine each day, and by sending in a sample to be examined.

4.   How can you help to keep mothers from having convulsions?

Answer: You can help to keep mothers from having convulsions by being sure that they get rid of poisons and waste material:

a. Through the skin, by daily bath.

b. Through the bowels, by preventing constipation.

c. Through the kidneys, by being sure they are doing their work.

d. Through the lungs, by getting the mother to sleep and live in the fresh air.

5. What kind of diet should the mother have before the baby comes?

Answer: The mother should have a plain, simple diet. No fried food; very little meat; some green vegetables and fruit every day; plenty of milk and eight glasses of water every day.

6. What must you teach the mother about rest, sleep and exercise?

Answer: You must teach the mother that she should have short periods of complete rest several times daily. She should have eight hours of sleep every night. She should have some exercise out of doors each day. She should not work to make herself very tired. She should do no heavy lifting.

7. What should you teach the mother about her clothing?

Answer: You should teach the mother that all clothing should hang from the shoulders, and that there should be no bands such as garters and waistbands. That she should wear low heeled and broad toed shoes.

8. What can be done for sunken nipples?

Answer: The nipples should be gently drawn out by putting over them the mouth of a bottle, from which hot water has been poured, or with the fingers.

9. Should a mother visit a dentist while pregnant?

Answer: Yes. It is important that the teeth be in good order. They should be brushed two or three times a day. The mother should eat good nourishing food.

10. What should you do for varicose veins?

Answer: For Varicose veins you should show the patient how to raise the leg by placing chair upside down in bed, padding with pillow and resting limb on back of chair.

11. What are the danger signals?

Answer: The danger signals are vomiting, headaches, dizziness, specks before the eyes, swelling of the feet, hands or eyelids, scanty urine neuralgic pains, and bleedings.

LESSON III

1. What should the mother prepare for her delivery?

Answer: The mother should prepare gowns, sheets, pillow cases, paper pads, clean rags that have been boiled (ironed with a hot iron and put away in a flour sack which has been boiled,) one half pound of absorbent cotton, tub, two basins, oil cloth for bed, tea kettle of hot water that has been boiled, safety pins and towels boiled and ironed.

2. What should the mother have ready for the baby?

Answer: The mother should have:

   a. A clothes basket or a bed made out of a box.

   b. Supplies: Lard or vaseline, castile or ivory soap, soft wash clothes; small box of cotton wool; safety pins, large and small; soft towels; soft blanket to receive baby; one folded blanket, pad or pillow for mattress.

   c. Clothes: Three abdominal bands with ties; two dozen diapers; three shirts, cotton and wool; four night gowns; one 36-inch square flannelette

3. What equipment should a midwife carry with her?

Answer: A midwife should carry a hand bag with loose washable lining; liquid soap for washing hands, sterile absorbent cotton, nail brush for scrubbing hands, blunt scissors for cutting baby's cord; nail file for cleaning nails; two towels, one or more packages, each containing two dressings for cords and two cord tapes.

4. How would you prepare the package containing cord dressing, tape etc?

Answer: You should take a piece of white cloth that is soft and has been washed and boiled, cut two pieces 6 inches wide and 6 inches long for cord dressings. Fold each piece twice. Make a slit with scissors half way through one folded square. Place together. Place cord tapes on dressings and fold over. Wrap these up in another piece of heavy cloth and pin together with pins. Make several of these at one time and place in oven with medium size potato. When potato is done, remove packages from oven and leave them pinned up until ready for use.

5. What do you mean by "sterile"?

Answer: By "Sterile," you mean when an article has been freed from germs.

6. How may things be sterilized?

Answer:

   a. By boiling for ten minutes.

   b. By baking for an hour.

7. How should you make a paper pad for a bed?

Answer: Iron newspapers with a hot iron, spread full size and lay one over the other until about one inch thick, cover with a piece of cloth that has been boiled and ironed with a hot iron. Turn edges of cloth and sew unto paper.

LESSON 1V

1. Name stages of labour?

Answer: the first stage of labour is from a few minutes to eighteen hours. Pains like cramps, first in back, then in front, recurring at regular intervals, gradually recurring more frequently. The second stage, from a few minutes to two hours, usually begins with rupture of bag of water; pains harder, more frequent, bearing down in character bulging perineum, delivery of head, shoulders, body. The third stage is about half an hour between birth of child and expulsion of placenta (afterbirth).

2. What would you do if there were haemorrhage (bleeding) before birth of baby?

Answer: If haemorrhages occur before the birth of the baby, you should call a physician immediately. Keep patient absolutely quiet.

3. What would you do if there were excessive haemorrhage (bleeding) immediately after the birth of the baby?

Answer: If haemorrhages took place immediately after the birth of the baby you should send for a physician. Meanwhile rub the womb, occasionally squeezing on it to express the clots of blood. Keep the hand on the womb to see that it remains small and hard. Put cold towels or ice to abdomen. Keep patient quiet.

4. What would you do if afterbirth or hand presented?

Answer: If the afterbirth or hand presented you should call a physician immediately. Keep patient calm and quiet as possible.

5. If the child's feet or buttocks come first, what must the midwife do?

Answer: If the child's feet or buttocks come first the midwife should lift the feet up over the mother's abdomen and hold them there to help the head come through. If the head does not come through in a few minutes the baby will be dead.

6. What would you do if there were a tear of the perineum?

Answer: If there were a tear in the perineum you should call a physician. In the meanwhile, put a sterile pad against the perineum.

7. How long would you wait during labour before calling a physician if the labour were hard with no results?

Answer: If the labour were hard with no results, you should call a physician in eighteen hours or less.

8. What attention would you give the eyes immediately after birth?

Answer: Immediately after birth you should FIRST WASH YOUR HANDS THOROUGHLY; then cleanse the baby's face. Then, according to instructions in package of eye-drops furnished to midwives by the Department of Health, drop into each eye two drops.

9. How long would you wait before cutting cord?

Answer: Before cutting cord, you should wait until pulse in cord stops beating.

10. How would you tie the cord?

Answer: To tie the cord, you should FIRST WASH YOUR HANDS. Press the places to be tied between thumb and finger, one and two inches from body, then pass sterile tape around the cord twice, draw tight and tie in square knot. Repeat for second tie and cut between. If the cord bleeds, put another tape around back of the one already on, and tie tightly before removing the first. Never dress cord until tied so that there is no bleeding.

11. How would you dress the cord?

Answer: To dress the cord you should FIRST WASH YOUR HANDS; no grease of any kind to be used. With clean hands remove cord dressing from package; wrap cord lightly in slit dressing; place second dressing on top; lay up and over to left side and put on abdominal binder tight enough to hold dressing in place.

12. What would you do if the baby did not breathe at first?

Answer: If the baby did not breathe at first, you should:
   a. Cleanse the mouth and nose so that passage to lungs are free.
   b. Grasp child firmly by feet, holding over bed, and slap sharply on back.
   c. Put child in basin of warm water, being careful to keep head well out of water, and sprinkle cold water on chest.
   d. Hold the head of child in one hand, which also supports the shoulders, and hold the legs between the thumb, index and middle fingers of the other hands; then slowly bend the body so as to bring the thighs up against the chest; then return to the extended position. This should be done at the rate of 15 to 18 per minute.

13. How long should you continue artificial respiration?

Answer: You should continue artificial respiration as long as the baby's heart beats.

LESSON V

1. What should midwife do on arrival at case?

Answer: On arrival at case, the midwife should have a good fire, put scissors wrapped in clean and white cotton cloth, nail brush and nail cleaner in pan for washing hands, cover the water and let boil for several minutes. Have more water boiling in tea kettle. Place clean towel on table or chair beside mother's bed, and place on it one package containing tape and cord dressing, have cotton ready for use. Place a large tub under bed.

2. How would you prepare patient for delivery?

Answer: To prepare a patient for delivery, you should give a simple warm water enema. (The enema should not be given if bag of water has broken.) After your hands have been prepared, remove a small portion of cotton and wash abdomen and inside thighs with soap suds. Then wash private parts. Use at least ten different pieces of cotton. Be sure to begin at the top and wipe downward, being sure to throw the cotton away at the end of each stroke.

Repeat this process, as soap suds were used. Midwife must deliver patient in bed.

3. How would you prepare your patient's bed for labour?

Answer: To prepare your patient's bed you should put on a sheet and tuck it well under the mattress at the head and sides; across the middle of the bed, place a large piece of rubber sheeting doubled in the middle and tuck well under the sides, and on this the delivery pad. Put on the top sheet, blanket and counter pane, but don't, even at the foot, tuck these covers. There may be a pillow if the patient wishes.

4. How would you prepare your hands for delivery of case?

Answer: For the delivery of a case, see that nails are cut short, then clean under nails with nail file. Scrub hands and arms up above elbows with nail brush, soap and water, paying special attention to the nails and being careful not to miss any area inside of the fingers. Scrub each hand and arm for five minutes.

5. How can a midwife best protect her patient from child-bed fever?

Answer: A midwife can best protect her patient from child-bed fever by having everything about herself and patient clean, and making no inside examinations. The midwife should also wash her own hands frequently in soap and water. She should never attend a case of confinement after being on a case of contagious disease or pus infection.

6. What do you consider normal time for deliver of the after-birth?

Answer: Normal time for delivery of after-birth is from ten to thirty minutes.

7. How long would you wait before calling a doctor to deliver the after-birth?

Answer: Before calling a doctor to deliver after-birth a midwife should wait one hour.

8. What would you do to help in the delivery of the after-birth?

Answer: To help in the delivery of the placenta, a midwife should wait one-half hour then gently knead (rub in a circular motion) the stomach above the navel. This will help to contract the uterus (womb) and expel after-birth. You should never pull on the cord.

9. How would you know that after-birth was whole?

Answer: You would know that the after-birth was whole by careful examination. The outside layer of skin should be whole, and there would be no ragged edges or holes.

10. What would you do if part of afterbirth was not passed?

Answer: If only a part of the after-birth were passed, a midwife should call a doctor immediately.

11. What should a midwife say when sending for a doctor?

Answer: When sending for a doctor a midwife should give the patient's name, tell the nearest way to reach her house and say what the trouble is, so the doctor will know what to bring.

12. Describe in detail the proper care of the mother immediately following the birth of the baby, and after-birth.

Answer: In caring for the mother after the birth of the baby, first wash hands. Cleanse the private parts. Place a sterile pad against the vulva and pin on stomach binder; put on clean gown, remove dirty pads and linen from bed, replace with clean pad and linen. Do not disturb more than necessary but watch carefully for first six hours for excessive bleeding. Call doctor at once if necessary.

LESSON VI

1. How long should a woman remain in bed following child-birth?

Answer: Following child-birth, a woman should remain in bed at least ten days; longer if mother is weak.

2. What would you do if the mother could not urinate (pass water)?

Answer: If the mother could not urinate, you should put cloths wrung out of hot water over bladder. Pour water from vessel to vessel in sight of patient. Place patient on bedpan containing small amount of hot water. Pour warm water over private parts.

3. How long would you try these simple methods before calling for a doctor?

Answer: Before calling a doctor, you should try these methods, certainly not more than twelve hours.

4. Describe care of mother following child-birth?

Answer: To care for the mother following child-birth:

    a. Bring to the bedside everything that will be needed:

        1. Two towels,
        2. washcloth,
        3. comb and brush,
        4. clean sheets, and pillow cases,
        5. clean gown,
        6. soap,
        7. water in basin.

    b. Bath: Proceed in the following order: Bathe face, ears, neck, chest, arms, hands, abdomen, thighs, legs, feet, back and private parts. Dry each part immediately after washing. Protect the bed by placing a bath towel under each part as you wash it. Add hot water as necessary. Have water very hot.

    c. Remove all covers except sheet; in winter use on blanket instead of sheet.

    d. To change patient's gown: Have patient lie on back with legs drawn up; pull gown up as far as you can; have patient raise her thighs slightly and draw gown up to neck; draw sleeves off, slip gown over the head and off the other arm. The clean gown is put on in the same way as the soiled was removed. Begin by putting one arm into sleeve; put gown over head; draw other arm into sleeve; the gown is them pulled down.

    e. To comb hair: Part hair in middle from front to back: turn head and comb first one side and then the other; plait each side after combing it out.

    f. To change patient's bed: Be sure to have everything necessary at hand; loosen the bed clothes on all sides; remove the spread and blankets, leaving the sheet over patient (or if weather is cold, one blanket instead of sheet); turn patient on her side near edge of bed; roll the under sheet as near the patient as possible; cover the bare side of mattress with clean sheet tucking it in well and being sure there are no wrinkles; turn patient over on clean sheet, remove soiled sheet; then cover the rest of the bed with clean sheet, tucking it well; place a clean sheet over the soiled top sheet that is to be removed, cover this with a blanket if necessary; pullout soiled sheet from foot of bed, while patient holds the clean one in place. Tuck clean sheet and blanket at foot of bed; put other blankets on if needed, and then put on spread.

5.   Should a midwife give vaginal douches?

Answer: A midwife should NEVER GIVE A VAGINAL DOUCHE WITHOUT A DOCTOR'S ORDER.

6.   What diet should a mother have while in bed?

Answer: While in bed a mother should have a light diet; no fried food, plenty of milk, cereals and pure fresh water, and vegetables.

7.   Describe breast feeding with reference to time and immediate care of breasts.

Answer: Baby should be put to breast eight hours after birth, and at regular intervals of three hours thereafter. Nipples should be cleaned with boiled water before and after each nursing. Baby should nurse fifteen to twenty minutes.

8.   What would you do to increase quantity of mother's milk?

Answer: to increase quantity of mother's milk, give liquids such as fresh cow's milk, cocoa, corn meal gruel.

9.   What else would you do if mother did not have enough milk for the baby?

Answer: If mother did not have enough milk for baby, you should:
   a. Put baby to both breasts at each feeding period.
   b. See that the mother is getting proper nourishing food, sufficient rest and sleep, and is free from worry
   c. If mother does not have enough milk, evaporated (tinned) or cows milk will have to be used as well.

10.   Why should a mother always nurse her baby if possible?

Answer: A mother should always nurse her baby if possible, because there is no perfect substitute for mother's milk. Baby has best chance for life and health with natural food, and mother herself does better.

11.   When should a mother not nurse her baby?

Answer: A mother should not nurse her baby if she had tuberculosis, or is very sick.

LESSON VII

1.   What is the best food for baby?

Answer: The best food for the baby is mother's milk.

2.   If the mother is unable to nurse the baby, what is the next best food?

Answer: If the mother is unable to nurse the baby, the next best food is cow's milk, modified.

3. Why should a baby never be given anything except (warm) water until milk comes into the mother's breasts?

Answer: A baby should never be given anything except warm water until the milk comes into the mother's breasts because fluid which is in the breasts before the milk comes acts as a purgative and cleanses the baby's bowels and prepares them for food. Food might upset the baby's digestive organs and unfit them to receive the mother's milk when it does come.

4. How would you bathe the baby?

Answer: The baby's first bath should be given by applying olive oil or lard with a soft cloth, being sure that no grease comes in contact with or even near the baby's cord. After the first day, baby should have a daily bath with warm water and castile or ivory soap.

5. What is the most important thing in a baby's life?

Answer: The most important thing in a baby's life is regularity and protection. Regular hours for feeding, regular hours for sleeping.

6. How should a baby sleep?

Answer: The baby should sleep alone. He should not be rocked or held while sleeping. He should have plenty of fresh air.

7. What are the three things to remember in caring for a premature baby?

Answer: In caring for a premature baby, the three things to remember are:

    a. Keep it warm

    b. Feed it with mother's milk

    c. Do not handle for any purpose

8. What advise would you give the mother on dismissal of a case?

Answer: On dismissal of a case, you should advise the mother to eat nutritious foods, take sufficient rest, and nurse her baby regularly at three-hour intervals. Bathe it daily. If baby is ill, stop all feeding except boiled water and call a doctor. Do not delay; call a doctor at first sign of danger as little babies soon die if neglected.

9. What are the most important things you should learn from these lessons?

Answer: The most important things you should learn from these lessons are:

    a. WHEN YOU SHOULD CALL A DOCTOR

    b. THAT YOU MUST BE CLEAN

    c. THE TERRIBLE RESPONSIBILITY THAT LIES IN YOUR HANDS

Notes

Chapter 1

1. Some of my respondents requested that their true identities be withheld. A few older midwives, for example, were shy about their names appearing in print. Several present-day midwives in large hospitals made the same plea, some even fearing that bureaucratic administrators reading this book might take exception to their critical remarks. Given these preferences for anonymity, I decided to conceal the identities of all midwives, assigning them either a fictitious name or referring to them by work site only.

2. I employ the terms birthing women, pregnant women, birthing clients, expectant mothers, and female patients interchangeably, following the usage of my respondents.

3. This favourable assessment of hospital births by local Burgeo clients is confirmed by a recent Canadian study of mothers in Manitoba. As Luxton (1980:100) states: "Whatever their opinions, women unanimously noted one major advantage that hospital births have over home births. It is socially acceptable for a woman giving birth to spend four or five days in hospital where she is not responsible for anything. Women considered their hospital stays as vacations or holidays."

4. The recent bureaucratization of maternity services has been accompanied by a failure by the Newfoundland and Labrador government to renew the Midwives' Act, and it has become increasingly difficult for trained midwives to gain a licence to practise midwifery as an autonomous profession. Geographic isolation has so far left midwifery largely intact in many areas of the province, however. There, the local health board recruits trained midwives, whose salaries are paid by the provincial government, to staff their maternity wards. In one small cottage hospital where I carried out observations of midwives and birthing clients, for example, midwives still manage the maternity ward with little interference from physicians and administrators, delivering

most babies and calling on the doctor in attendance only in cases of abnormality.

5. Sociological definitions of professionalism are highly diverse, and include those that range from a relatively mild (Millerson 1964; Parsons 1951; Ben-David 1963) to a highly critical assessment of the professionalisation process (Freidson 1970; Parkin 1979; Johnson 1972). Most sociologists view occupations as professions if they possess most or all of the following characteristics: a body of specialised systematic knowledge and technical skills; formal training to acquire these skills; application of specialised learning and technical know-how in order to maintain or improve public services; a code of ethics to ensure professional standards; state licence and power to accredit new members and exclude those without formal credentials; relative autonomy from administrators, clients and neighbouring occupational groups, and association membership for the purpose of establishing control over their specialty. It is on this basis that professions are normally awarded high economic and social standing. Some sociologists (Larson 1977; Freidson 1986), however, maintain that it is the political power of professions over social institutions and clients, not genuine expertise, that leads to elite privilege. The recent tendency of professionals to work in bureaucratic organisations has led some sociologists (Derber 1982) to conclude that professional autonomy is on the wane, that service employees are being deprofessionalised and even proletarianised as they are subjected to organisational controls. As I attempt to show in this book, Newfoundland and Labrador midwives working in small organisations satisfy most of the sociological criteria required for professional standing. Such professionalism has been greatly eroded, however, for midwives employed in large regional and teaching hospitals.

6. Scopolamine, an alkaloid extracted from the solanaceous plant, acts as a sedative and a mild analgesic. When used together with morphine, it produces a state commonly known as 'twilight sleep.' When successfully mixed and monitored, the result is forgetfulness rather than blockage of labour pain.

7. As Leavitt (1980) notes, these early feminists had a point. For although it may appear from today's standpoint that women in the early decades of this century ceded control of their birth to doctors by choosing anaesthesia, many of them were in fact making *conscious* decisions concerning their labours by going to sleep.

8. For an in-depth discussion of the American women's movement, especially concerning its splintering into isolated groups oriented around single issue concerns, see Ruzek 1978 and Segal 1987.

9. The increasing bureaucratisation of the NHS by the Conservative-led government in present-day Britain has been accompanied by an attempt to cut state funding and even to delegate certain health services to private corporations. These developments have created additional

difficulties blocking midwives' professionalism, including abysmally low salaries for midwifery practitioners at all levels of the hospital hierarchy as well as increased stress for senior midwives forced to deal with, in many workplaces, severe staff shortages and ever-dwindling budgets (Kitzinger 1988:24–ff).

10. According to the medical historian, Edward Shorter (1982:59), "[c]onstantly tugging and hauling at the mother's birth canal, at the infant's head, and at the placenta, [traditional lay midwives] were captives of a folkloric view that the best midwife is the one who interferes most."

11. Not all feminists involved in the recent health care movement share this non-critical view of traditional midwifery. According to British sociologist S. Macintyre (1977), the appeal to a former unsullied period in which childbirth was a rewarding, painfree, and safe female life event unhampered by outside control and intervention is based on assumptions which lack evidence.

12. This assumption of a growing professional dominance is controversial. According to McKinlay (1982) and Ritzer and Walczak (1988), for example, these features of organisational employment not only characterise the work worlds of emerging and semi-professional service occupations but have begun to permeate elite professions, such as medicine. The once autonomous and powerful physician, it is argued, is becoming a narrowly specialised bureaucratic employee with limited work discretion. There exist to date few concrete data to support this claim, however. Feminists writing on health care tend to take exception to this assumption made by some deprofessionalisation writers, and instead continue to exclude medicine from the deprofessionalisation process.

13. The infant mortality rate in Newfoundland and Labrador (combining neonatal and post-neonatal rates) in 1922 was approx. 116 per 1,000 live births. This is comparable to the situation in present-day developing countries (Pott *et al.* 1983). By 1950, the provincial rate had dropped by more than half, to around 45 and steadily decreased thereafter, with approx. 24 per 1,000 at the period signifying the demise of the cottage hospital system in the mid-1960s, a figure that is close to the Canadian rate at the time. Maternal mortality rates had likewise noticeably fallen between the period under study, from a high of 6.2 per 1,000 live births in 1923, dropping to 4.1 by 1950 and declining to 1.4 by 1966. Of course, these improvements in infant and maternal outcomes were in part due to an overall rise in the standard of living. According to local medical professionals and health authorities, however, the care given by cottage hospital midwives also contributed significantly to this improvement in mortality statistics throughout the period under review. See, for example, Ross 1965. Source of mortality statistics: Department of Health: Government of Newfoundland and Labrador, *Annual Report*— 1953 and 1977, St. John's, Nfld., 1978; Department of Health: Government of Newfoundland and Labrador, *Outline: Child and*

Maternal Health— Province of Newfoundland and Labrador, St. John's, Nfld., 1966.

14. Historical source: Nevitt, 1978. Recent trends: Report of the Royal Commission on Hospital and Nursing Home Costs to the Government of Newfoundland and Labrador, St. John's, Newfoundland, February 1984.

15. Statistics on midwives trained in vocational programs during the heyday of the cottage hospital system are absent from provincial Department of Health records. Midwifery is not unique in this regard, however; records of graduates from the training programs of other service occupations, including nursing and medicine, are also inconsistent or lacking altogether. Inquiry at the Newfoundland and Labrador Nursing Union (NLNU) concerning historical records yielded little solid information. The NLNU, in fact, does not even collect statistics on present-day nurse-midwives. I was able to unearth only one figure—by 1926, 60 trainees had successfully completed the midwifery course offered by the Midwives' Club during its first five years of operation. See the photo on page 93 and on the cover of two classes of graduating midwives from the Midwives' Club. Reports in the succeeding decades by the Department of Health contain references, however, to locally trained midwives staffing the cottage hospitals. Source: *The Newfoundland Quarterly*, vols. 24 & 25, 1924–25, 1925–26. See also various references to midwifery training in Nevitt, 1978.

Chapter 2

1. Reflecting the cross-national pattern, the transformation of midwifery in Canada shows significant heterogeneity. According to Laforce (1990), by the mid-19th century midwifery in Quebec was a well-adapted profession; after formal instruction and examination, midwives were granted government license to practice. Many took employment in the newly emerging maternity clinics founded in Quebec City and Montreal in order to aid poor women during childbirth (p. 40). This situation of Quebec midwifery closely parallels my own findings on the development of midwifery in Newfoundland and Labrador, except for the fact that midwifery there escaped bureaucratisation and medicalisation for a longer period than Quebec.

2. For a description of the situation of newly arriving immigrants in what was then referred to as "new France" (present-day Quebec), see Abbott, 1931.

3. The decision to train nurses rather than midwives reflects interprofessional rivalries among medicine, nursing and midwifery that continue even today. Whereas in Britain the *Midwives' Act* of 1902 established a formal training program for examination and certification of midwives, in central Canada, like in many American states, the powerful Ontario medical association pressured the government to institute strict controls over midwives and eventually to ban midwifery practice altogether. Ontario nursing, influenced by the Nightingale view of the

"ideal nurse" as showing wifely obedience to the doctor while at the same time attempting to establish nursing as an independent profession, refrained from challenging doctors on the issue of care of pregnant women and their newborns.

Chapter 3

1. Social scientists have studied this mode of exchange common in various traditional societies. See Kropotkin 1972 [1912]; Mauss 1967 [1951]; Sahlins 1965.

2. See, for example, Ehrenreich 1978; Conrad & Schneider 1980; Starr 1982.

3. Of course, caregiver expertise and adequate equipment are not the only determinants of successful birth outcomes. Infant mortality is closely linked, among other factors, to clients' diet and sanitary conditions.

4. However, as a granny midwife narrates, "a lot of the women in the old times didn't have much milk."

5. The premier of the time, Joseph Smallwood, stressed that resettlement was 'voluntary'; no one would be uprooted from their natal community unwillingly. However, as House (1978:122) notes, "resettlement was meant to be 'voluntary,' but it is clear that the government could entice people to volunteer to move by cutting off their local services."

6. The regionalisation of maternity-care services in large hospitals and the subsequent closing of cottage hospitals has inevitably increased the amount of time some birthing women are separated from their families, friends and community. In an attempt to soften the blow of separation from significant others during pre-delivery period, the provincial government has provided funds for boarding houses or hostels adjacent to some regional hospitals. In the case of native women, translators have also been hired to help bridge the cultural gap between clients and hospital attendants.

7. For a discussion of the effect of the malpractice industry on present-day U.S. midwives see O'Reilly *et al.* 1986.

Chapter 4

1. Melosh (1982:21–2) notes a similar 'traditionalist perspective' among American lay nurses. Women's apparently natural gifts of moral superiority and religious devotion to service, it was believed, make them particularly suited to nursing the sick.

2. "Blue milk" contrasts with colostrum, i.e. the white milk that is secreted for a few days before and after childbirth.

3. An outport is a small coastal settlement. Residents of the outports are typically referred to as "outporters." Sometimes more belittling labels such as "baymen/women" or "baywop" are used.

4. Such shortcomings were not unique to the Newfoundland and Labrador midwifery apprenticeship system. See, for example, Laget (1980) on

similar perils associated with lay midwifery in 17th- and 18th-century France.

5. Similar developments occurred elsewhere in North America and Europe at earlier periods. See, for example, Rosenberg, 1979.

6. This style of recruitment was also typical of vocational programs for training midwives in other areas of the West during the early modern period. See, for example, Laget (1980:157–73) on formal midwifery schooling in 17th- and 18th-century France.

7. Melosh (1982:67) makes a similar point regarding the vocational schooling of nursing students in the U.S. prior to World War II: 'Set apart from the social life of their contemporaries, young women participated in a communal life arranged around work. Theirs was a woman's world: they enjoyed the camaraderie of other women as peers, and looked up to female models as they worked with more experienced students and supervisors. Few other institutions in the 20th century could provide young women with a comparable experience of female autonomy. Seldom explicitly feminist in their ideology, the schools nonetheless empowered young nurses as women by expecting much of them, and by denying the cultural contradiction between femininity and commitment to work.'

8. The manual contained: (1) a number of 'birth reports' which certified midwives were required to fill out within a specified period after each homebirth; (2) a list of 'midwifery safety rules,' including prenatal instruction, daily care of mother and newborn during the lying-in period, and general information concerning antiseptic techniques, the proper use of laxatives, enemas, and silver nitrate drops for infants' eyes to prevent blindness by gonorrhoeal infection, as well as the ways to recognise the vital signs of impending abnormality, such as prolonged labour; breech, transverse and cross presentations; haemorrhaging or fever of the expectant mother and puerperal eclampsia; (3) a series of seven lessons titled 'questions and answers on midwife's work'; and (4) advice on diet during pregnancy. Appendix II presents the manual in its original form.

9. My subsequent postdoctoral research on clients' views of midwifery in historical perspective indicates that many expectant mothers regret the disappearance of the cottage hospital midwives, who did not rush them through the birth process aided by impersonal technology, only in order to desert them immediately after delivery.

10. It is important to note that the vast majority of those midwives holding formal credentials (if not a licence to practise) in both Newfoundland and Labrador and in Canada as a whole received their training in a vocational program abroad. But there exists, to my knowledge, no reliable statistics concerning the exact numbers of vocationally- versus academically-trained midwives.

11. As noted above, the transformation of midwives into university degree holders is a recent phenomenon confined mainly to North America, with

France being a notable exception on the other side of the Atlantic. French midwifery students now train for three years, graduating with academic rather than vocational qualifications, as is still the case in most other European countries. Similar developments are now being discussed among British midwifery educators as well. Of course, academisation of occupational socialisation is hardly unique to midwifery. On the contrary, schooling of neophytes in universities has been a typical strategy of most service workers attempting to upgrade their occupation to an 'intellectual discipline' (Hughes 1971). This has been the route as well of the traditional 'gentlemen professions' of medicine, law and the ministry (Carr-Saunders 1933), as well as of 19th-century medical and paramedical craftworkers—toothpullers [dentists], apothecaries [pharmacists], horsedoctors [veterinarians] and engineers (Ackerknecht and Fischer-Homberger 1977).

Chapter 5

1. This is not to suggest that present-day North American lay midwives working in homes have poor mortality outcomes. Statistics show that they, like their counterparts in the Netherlands, have impressive birth outcomes, at a par with and in some cases even lower than nurse-midwives working in birth centres with similar low-risk mothers (for U.S. data see Sullivan & Weitz 1988; for Canadian data see Barrington 1985; Burtch 1988).

2. There exist few sociological studies which focus upon the variable of organisational scale in determining professionalism for specific service occupations. For an exception, see Evers, Bohlen and Warren 1976.

3. To quote Potts *et al.* (1983:xi–xii) on some of the most serious problems now confronting policy makers in the developing world: "There were approximately 130 million births in the world in 1980. By the year 2000, this number will reach 163 million. Nearly all this increase in births will occur in developing regions of the world, where 85 percent of births and 95 percent of perinatal deaths are expected to occur by the year 2000. In the last two decades of this century, 40 million infants will die in the perinatal period if present rates continue. In all, 250 million or more infant and child deaths will occur. The vast majority of these deaths would be considered preventable by developed-country standards...Although most developing countries have some maternity hospitals in which high-risk deliveries are managed, many are overcrowded and must struggle to provide adequate care with limited financial resources, personnel and facilities."

4. What needs to be more fully considered, of course, is whether the resources now exist that allow for a more decentralised midwifery profession. Unlike the old grannies, today's U.S. and Canadian midwives working at home can carry oxygen, ultrasound, and other equipment, and most can get their (predominantly middle class) clients to hospital easily if need arises (Sullivan & Weitz 1988).

References

Abbott, A. 1988 *The System of Professions*. Chicago: University of Chicago Press.

Abbott, M. 1931 *History of Medicine in the Province of Quebec*. Toronto: Macmillan.

Ackerknecht, E. 1967 *Medicine at the Paris Hospital 1994–1848*. Baltimore: The John Hopkins Press.

_____ and E. Fischer-Homberger 1977 "Five Made It—One Not: The Rise of Medical Craftsmen to Academic Status during the 19th Century." *Clio Medico*, 12(4):255–67.

Adler, J. 1979 *Artists in Offices*. New Brunswick, N.J.: Transaction Books.

Agar, M. H. 1980 *The Professional Stranger*. New York: Academic Press.

_____ 1985 *Independents Declared: The Dilemma of Independent Trucking*. Washington, D. C.: Smithsonian Institution.

Albrecht, G. & J. Levy 1982 "The Professionalisation of Osteopathy: Adaptation in the Medical Marketplace." In J. Roth (ed.), *Research in the Sociology of Health Care*, pp. 161–206. Greenwich, Conn.: JAI Press, Inc.

Aldrich, H. E. and S. Mindlin 1978 "Uncertainty and Dependence: Two Perspectives on Environment." In L. Karpit (ed.), *Organisation and Environment*, pp. 149–70. Beverly Hills, Calif.: Sage.

_____ and J. Pfeffer 1976 "Environments of Organizations." *Annual Review of Sociology*, 2:79–105.

Alford, R. 1975 *Health Care Politics*. Chicago: The University of Chicago Press.

Ammar, H. 1954 *Growing Up in an Egyptian Village*. London: Routledge & Kegan Paul.

Anisef, P. and P. Basson 1979 "The Institutionalisation of a Profession: A Comparison of British and American Midwifery." *Sociology of Work and Occupations*, 6(3):353–72.

Arms, S. 1975 *Immaculate Deception: A New Look at Women and Childbirth in America*. San Francisco: San Francisco Book Co.

Arney, W. 1980 "Maternal-Infant Bonding: The Politics of Falling in Love with Your Child." *Feminist Studies*, 6(3):547–70.

Aronowitz, S. 1973 *False Promises: The Shaping of American Working Class Consciousness*. New York: McGraw-Hill.

Auerbach, E. 1968 "Black Midwives in Mississippi: The Professionalising of a Folk Role," *Human Mosaic*, 3:125–32.

Barrington, E. 1985 *Midwifery is Catching*. Toronto: NC Press.

Barber, B. 1952 *Science and the Social Order*. New York: The Free Press.

Becker, H.S. 1963 *Outsiders: Studies in the Sociology of Deviance*. New York: Free Press.

_____ 1966 "Introduction" to Clifford Shaw. *The Jack-Roller: A Delinquent Boy's Own Story*, rev. edn, pp. x–xviii. Chicago: University of Chicago Press [1925].

_____ 1970 *Sociological Work*. Chicago: Aldine.

_____ B. Geer and E.C. Hughes 1968 *Making the Grade: The Academic Side of Student Life*. New York: John Wiley and Sons.

_____ B. Geer, E.C. Hughes and A. L. Strauss 1961 *Boys in White*. Chicago: University of Chicago Press.

Bell, D. 1976 *The Cultural Contradictions of Capitalism*. New York: Basic Books.

_____ 1980 *The Winding Passage: Essays and Sociological Journeys*, 1960–80. Cambridge. Mass.: ABT Books.

Bendix, R. 1984 *Force, Fate, and Freedom: On Historical Sociology*. Berkeley: University of California Press.

Benoit, C. 1982 "The Poverty of Mothering: A Case Study of Women in a Newfoundland Community." Unpublished M. A. thesis. St. John's, Newfoundland: Memorial University of Newfoundland.

_____ 1987 "Uneasy Partners: Midwives and Their Clients." *Canadian Journal of Sociology*, 12:275–84.

_____ 1990 Mothering in a Newfoundland Community: 1900–1940." In K. Arnup, E. Levesque and R. Roach Pierson (eds.), *Delivering Motherhood: Maternal Ideologies in the 19th and 20th Centuries*. London: Routledge.

Benson, K. J. 1973 "An Analysis of Bureaucratic-Professional Conflict: Functional Versus Dialectical Approaches." *The Sociological Quarterly*, 14:376–94.

_____ 1978 "The Interorganisational Network as a Political Economy." In L. Karpit (ed.), *Organization and Environment*, pp. 69–101. London: Sage.

Berger, P. and T. Luckmann 1967 *The Social Construction of Reality*. New York: Doubleday.

Berkhofer, R. F. 1974 "The Political Context of a New Indian History." In N. Hundley and V. Deloria (eds.), *The American Indian*, 101–26. Santa Barbara: Clio Books.

Bernard, J. 1974 *The Future of Motherhood*. New York: Penguin Books.

Betz, M. and L. O'Connell 1983 "Changing Doctor-Patient Relationships and the Rise of Concern for Accountability." *Social Problems*, 31:84–95.

Biernacki, P. 1986 *Pathways from Heroin Addiction: Recovery Without Treatment*. Philadelphia: Temple University Press.

Bierstedt, R. 1974 *Power and Progress: Essays in Sociological Theory*. New York: McGraw-Hill.

Biggs, L. 1983 "The Case of the Missing Midwives: A History of Midwifery in Ontario from 1795–1900." *Ontario History*, 65(1):21–35.

_____ 1984 "The Response to Maternal Mortality in Ontario, 1920–1940." Thesis submitted in conformity with the requirements for the degree of Master of Science in the Division of Community Health at the University of Toronto, Toronto, Ontario.

Blau, P. M. and W. R. Scott 1972 "Organisational Development." In M. Brinkerhoff and P. Kunz (eds.), *Complex Organisations and Their Environments*, pp. 167–75. Dubuque, Iowa: Wm. C. Brown Co.

Bodemann, M. 1978 "A Problem of Sociological Practice: The Case for Interventive Observation in Field Work." *Theory and Society*, 5(4):387–420.

Boehme, G. 1984 "Midwifery as Science: An Essay on the Relationship Between Scientific and Everyday Knowledge." In N. Stehr and V. Meja (eds.), *Society and Knowledge: Contemporary Perspectives in the Sociology of Knowledge*, pp. 365–85. New Brunswick, N. J.: Transaction Books.

Boston Women's Health Book Collective 1976 *Our Bodies, Ourselves*. New York: Simon and Schuster, second edition.

Bowles, S. and H. Gintis 1976 *Schooling in Capitalist America*. London: Routledge & Kegan Paul.

Braude, L. 1975 *Work and Workers: A Sociological Analysis*. New York: Praeger.

Braverman, H.1974 *Labour and Monopoly Capital: The Degration of Work in the Twentieth Century*. New York: Monthly Review.

Breckinridge, M. 1927 "The Nurse-Midwife: A Pioneer," American Journal of Public Health, 1147–51.

Brinkerhoff, M. and P. Kunz 1972 *Complex Organisations and Their Environments*. Dubuque, Iowa: C. Brown Co.

Brym, R. J. 1980 *Intellectuals and Politics*. London: George Allen & Unwin.

_____ 1987 "The Political Sociology of Intellectuals." In A. Gagnon (ed.), *The Role of Intellectuals in Liberal Democracies*. New York: Praeger.

Bucher, R. & A. Strauss 1961 "Professions in Process," *The American Journal of Sociology*, 66:325–34.

Buckley, S. 1979 "Ladies or Midwives: Efforts to reduce Infant and Maternal Mortality." In L. Kealey (ed.), *A Not Unreasonable Claim*, pp. 131–49. Toronto: The Women's Press.

Burawoy, M. 1980 *Manufacturing Consent*. Chicago: The University of Chicago Press.

Burtch, B. 1988 "Midwifery and the State: The New Midwifery in Canada." In A. McLaren (ed.), *Gender and Society: Creating a Canadian Women's Sociology*, pp. 349–71. Toronto: Pitman Ltd.

Burgess, R.1984 *In the Field: An Introduction to Field Research*. London: George Allen & Unwin.

Byrman, A. 1984 "The Debate about Quantitative and Qualitative Research: A Question of Methods or Epistemology?" *The British Journal of Sociology*, 35(1):75–92.

Callaway, H. 1978 "The Most Essentially Female Thing of All: 'Giving Birth.'" In S. Ardner (ed.), *Defining Females*. New York: Halstead Press.

Campbell, M. 1946 *Folks Do Get Born*. New York: Rinehart.

Campbell, M. 1984 "Information Systems and Management of Hospital Nursing: A Study in the Social Organisation of Knowledge." Ph.D. Thesis. Toronto: University of Toronto.

Canniff, W. 1894 *History of the Medical Profession in Upper Canada, 1783–1850*. Toronto: W. Biggs.

Caplow, T. A. 1954 *The Sociology of Work*. Minneapolis: University of Minnesota Press.

Carchedi, G. 1983 *Problems in Class Analysis: Production, Knowledge and the Function of Capital*. London: Routledge & Kegan Paul.

Carr-Saunders, A. M. 1933 *Professions*. Oxford: Clarendon Press.

Cartwright, A.1979 *The Dignity of Labour?: A Study of Childbearing and Induction*. London: Tavistock.

Clegg, S. and D. Dunkerley 1980 *Organisation, Class and Control*. London: Routledge & Kegan Paul.

Clifford, J. and G. Marcus 1986 *Writing Culture: The Poetics and Politics of Ethnography*. Berkeley: University of California Press.

Cohen, M. D. and J. G. March 1972 *The American College President*. New York: McGraw-Hill Books Co.

Colburn, D. G. Torrance & J. Kaufert 1983 "Medical Dominance in Canada in Historical Perspective: The Rise and Fall of Medicine?" *International Journal of Health*, 13:407–32.

Comte, A. 1968 *System of Positive Polity [1851–4]*. New York: Burt Franklin.

Conrad, P. and J. W. Schneider 1980 *Deviance and Medicalisation*. St. Louis: C. V. Mosby Co.

Corwin, R. G. 1961 "The Professional Employee: A Study of Conflict in Nursing Roles." *American Journal of Sociology*, 66:604–15.

Cosbie, W. G.1975 *The Toronto General Hospital, 1819–1965: A Chronicle*. Toronto: Macmillan.

Coser, R. 1960 "Laughter Among Colleagues: A Study of the Social Functions of Humour Among the Staff of a Mental Hospital." *Psychiatry*, 23:81–95.

Dainton, C. 1961 *The Story of England's Hospitals*. London: Museum Press.

Damstra-Wijmenga, S.M.I. 1984 "Home Confinement: The Positive Results in Holland," *Journal of the Royal College of General Practitioners*, 34:425–30.

Danziger, S. 1986 "Male Doctor-Female Patient." In P. Eakins (ed.), *The American Way of Birth*. Philadelphia: Temple University Press.

Davies, C. 1979 "Organization Theory and the Organization of Health Care: A Comment on the Literature." *Social Science and Medicine*, 13 A:413–22.

_____ 1983 "Professionals in Bureaucracies: The Conflict Thesis Revisited." In R. Dingwall & P. Lewis (eds.), *The Sociology of the Professions*, pp. 177–94. New York: St. Martin's Press.

Davis, D. 1988 *Blood and Nerves: An Ethnographic Focus on Menopause*. St. John's: Memorial University of Newfoundland, Institute of Social and Economic Research.

Davis, F. (ed.) 1966 *The Nursing Profession: Five Sociological Essays*. New York: John Wiley & Sons.

De Vries, R. 1985 *Regulating Birth: Midwives, Medicine and the Law*. Philadelphia: Temple University Press.

_____ 1984 "'Humanising Childbirth': The Discovery and Implementation of Bonding Theory." *International Journal of Health Services*, 14(1):89–104.

Derber, C. 1982 *Professionals as Workers: Mental Labour in Advanced Capitalism*. Boston: G.K. Hall.

Devitt, N. 1979 "How Doctors Conspired to Eliminate the Midwife Even Though the Scientific Data Support Midwifery." In D. Stewart and L. Stewart (eds.), *Compulsory Hospitalisation: Freedom of Choice in Childbirth*, pp. 345–70. Marble Hill, Mo.: NAPSAC.

Dick-Read, G. 1944 *Childbirth Without Fear*. New York: Dell.

Dingwall, R. and P. Lewis (eds.) 1983 *The Sociology of the Professions*. New York: St. Martin's Press.

Donegan, J. 1978 *Women and Men Midwives*. Westport, Conn.: Greenview Press.

Donnison, J. 1977 *Midwives and Medical Men*. London: Heinemann.

_____ 1981 "The Development of the Occupation of Midwife: A Comparative View." *Midwife is a Labour of Love*, pp. 38–53. Vancouver: Press Gang.

Dougherty, M. 1982 "Southern Midwifery and Organised Health Care: Systems of Conflict." *Medical Anthropology*, 6(2):113–25.

Durkheim, E. 1933 *The Division of Labour in Society [1893]* trans. by G. Simpson. New York: Macmillan.

_____ 1952 *Suicide: A Study of Society [1897]*, trans. by J. A. Spaulding and G. Simpson. Glencoe, Ill.: The Free Press.

_____ 1957 *Professional Ethics and Civic Morals [1890–1900]*, trans. by C. Brookfield. London: Routledge & Kegan Paul.

_____ 1965 "A Durkheim Fragment: The Conjugal Family," [1891–2] trans. by G. Simpson, *American Journal of Sociology*, 70(5):527–36.

Eakins, P. 1986 *The American Way of Birth*. Philadelphia: Temple University Press.

Ebert, R. 1986 "America's Doctors, Medical Science, Medical Care." Daedalus, 115(2):55–81.

Ehrenreich, B. and D. English 1979 *For Her Own Good*. New York: Anchor Press.

_____ J. 1978 "Medicine and Social Control." In Ehrenreich, J. (ed.), *The Cultural Crisis of Modern Medicine*, pp. 39–79. New York: Monthly Review Press.

Elias, N. 1956 "Problems of Involvement and Detachment." *British Journal of Sociology*, 7:226–41.

Ellul, J. 1980 *The Technological System*, trans. by J. Neugroschel. New York: Continuum.

Emerson, R.A. 1981 "Observational Fieldwork." *Annual Review of Sociology*, 7:351–78.

Erneling, C. 1988 "Equality Between Women & Men in Sweden—Myth or Reality?" *Canadian Women's Studies*, 9(2):14–8.

Etzioni, A. (ed.) 1969 *The Semi-Professions and Their Organization*. New York: The Free Press.

Evers, F. J. Bohlen and R. Warren 1976 "The Relationship of Selected Size and Structural Indicators in Economic Organisations." *Administrative Science Quarterly*, 21:326–42.

Fabrega, H. 1971 "Some Features of Zinancetan Medical Knowledge." *Ethnology*, 9:25–43.

_____ and D. Silver 1970 "Some Social and Psychological Properties of Zinacanteco Shamans." *Behavioural Science*, 15:471–86.

Feldman, E. and M. Hurst 1987 "Outcomes and Procedures in Low Risk Birth: A Comparison of Hospital and Birth Centre Settings." *Birth*, 14(1):18–24.

Filstead, W.J. 1970 *Qualitative Methodology*. Chicago: Markham.

Forbes, T. 1966 *The Midwife and the Witch*. New Haven: Yale University Press.

Foster, P. 1989 "Improving the Doctor/Patient Relationship: A Feminist Perspective." *Journal of Social Policy*, 18(3):337–61.

Foucault, M. 1973 *The Birth of the Clinic [1963]*. London: Tavistock.

_____ 1979 *Discipline and Punish: The Birth of the Prison [1975]*. New York: Vintage Books.

_____ 1980 "The Politics of Health in the Eighteenth Century," [1976]. In M. Foucault *Power/Knowledge*, pp. 374–82. ed. by C. Gordon. New York: Pantheon Books.

Freidson, E. 1960 "Clients and Medical Practice." *American Journal of Sociology*, 65:374–82.

_____ 1970 *The Profession of Medicine: A Study in the Sociology of Applied Knowledge*. New York: Harper & Row.

_____ 1984 "The Changing Nature of Professional Control." *Annual Review of Sociology*, 10:1–20.

_____ 1986 *Professional Powers*. Chicago: University of Chicago Press.

Galbraith, J. K. 1967 *The New Industrial State*. New York: Signet.

Geertz, C. 1973 *The Interpretation of Cultures*. New York: Basic Books.

_____ 1983 *Local Knowledge*. New York: Basic Books.

Gilb, C. 1966 *Hidden Hierarchies: Professions and Government*. New York: Harper & Row.

Glaser, B. and A. Strauss 1976 *The Discovery of Grounded Theory*. Chicago: Aldine Publishing Co.

Glaser, W. 1970 *Social Settings and Medical Organisation: A Cross-National Study of the Hospital*. New York: Atherton Press.

Goffman, I. 1961 *Asylums*. New York: Anchor Books.

Goode, W. J. 1957 "Community Within a Community: The Professions." *American Sociological Review*, 22:194–200.

Gordon, L. 1976 *Women's Body Women's Right: A Social History of Birth Control in America*. New York: Grossman Publishing.

Gorz, A. 1964 *Strategy For Labour*. Boston: Beacon Press.

Goss, M. 1961 "Influence and Authority Among Physicians in an Outpatient Clinic." *American Sociological Review*, 26:39–50.

Gouldner, A. 1957, 1958 "Cosmopolitans and Locals: Toward an Analysis of Latent Social Roles—I & II." *Administrative Science Quarterly*, 2:281–306; 2:444–480.

_____ 1978 "The New Class Project, Part I." *Theory and Society*, 6(2):153–204.

_____ 1978 "The New Class Project, Part II." *Theory and Society*, 6(3):343–390.

Greenwood, E. 1957 "Attributes of a Profession." *Social Work*, 2:44–55.

Greer, G. 1984 *Sex and Destiny: The Politics of Human Fertility*. London: Secker & Warburg.

Gross, E. 1958 *Work and Society*. New York: Thomas Y. Crowell.

Gwyn, R. [1968], 1972 *Smallwood: The Unlikely Revolutionary*. Toronto: McClelland Stewart.

Habermas, J. 1971 *Knowledge and Human Interests [1968]*. London: Heinemann.

Haire, D. 1972 *The Cultural Warping of Childbirth*. Milwaukee: International Childbirth Education Association.

Hall, O. 1946 "The Informal Organisation of the Medical Profession." *Canadian Journal of Economics and Political Science*, 12:30–44.

_____ 1949 "Types of Medical Careers." *American Journal of Sociology*, 55:243–53.

Hall, R. H. 1968 "Professionalisation and Bureaucratisation." *American Sociological Review*, 33:92–104.

Halmos, P. 1966 *The Personal Service Society*. Cardiff: University College.

_____ 1973 *Professionalisation and Social Change*. Keele: University of Keele.

Hammond, P. (ed.) 1967 *Sociologists at Work*. New York: Doubleday Anchor.

Haug, M. R. 1973 "Deprofessionalisation: An Alternative Hypothesis for the Future." *Sociological Review Monograph*, 20:195–211.

_____ 1975 "The Deprofessionalisation of Everyone?" *Sociological Focus*, 3:197–213.

_____ and B. Lavin 1983 *Consumerism in Medicine: Challenging Physician Authority*. Beverly Hills: Sage.

_____ and M. Sussman 1969 "Professional Autonomy and the Revolt of the Client." *Social Problems*, 17:153–61.

Heinz, J. and E. Laumann 1982 *Chicago Lawyers: The Social Structure of the Bar*. New York: Russell Sage Foundation.

Heydebrand, W. 1985 "Technocracy and Neocorporatism: Toward a Theory of Organisational Change under Advanced Capitalism and Early State Socialism." *Current Perspectives in Social Theory*, 6:71–128.

Houd, S. and A. Oakley 1986 "Alternative Perinatal Services." In J.M.L. Phaff (ed.), *Perinatal Health Services in Europe*, pp. 17–47. London: Croom Helm.

Heitlinger, A. 1987 *Reproduction, Medicine and The Socialist State*. New York: St. Martin's Press.

Holmes, L. 1986 "African American Midwives in the South." In P. Eakins (ed.), *The American Way of Birth*, pp. 273–291. Philadelphia: Temple University Press.

House, J.D. 1978 *Newfoundland Society and Culture*. St. John's, Nfld.: Memorial University of Newfoundland.

Hughes, E. 1958 *Men and Their Work*. Glencoe, Ill.: The Free Press.

_____ 1966 "The Social Significance of Professionalisation." In H. Vollmer and D. Mills (eds.), *Professionalisation*, pp. 62–70. Englewood Cliffs, N. J.: Prentice-Hall.

_____ 1971 *The Sociological Eye*. Chicago: Aldine-Atherton.

Illich, I. 1971 *Deschooling Society*. New York: Harper & Row.

_____ 1977 *Limits to Medicine*. New York: Penguin Books.

Jackson, J. A. (ed.) 1970 *Professions and Professionalisation*. Cambridge: Cambridge University Press.

Johnson. T. 1972 *Professions and Power*. London: Macmillan.

Jordan, B. [1978] 1988 *Birth in Four Cultures: A Cross-Cultural Investigation of Childbirth in Yucatan, Holland, Sweden and the United States.* Montreal: Eden Press.

Katz, F. and H. Martin 1962 "Career Choice Processes." *Social Forces,* 41:149–54.

Kitzinger, S. 1972 *The Experience of Childbirth.* Harmondsworth: Penguin, third edition.

_____ (ed.) 1988 *The Midwife Challenge.* London: Pandora.

Klaus, M.H. and J.H. Kennell 1976 *Maternal-Infant Bonding.* St. Louis: Mosby.

Kobrin, F. 1966 "The American Midwife Controversy: A Crisis of Professionalisation." *Bulletin of the History of Medicine,* 40:350–63.

Kornhauser, W. 1963 *Scientists in Industry.* Berkeley: University of California Press.

Koch, S. 1985 "Malpractice Situation Once Again at Crisis Proportion." *Ob. Gyn. News,* 1–14.

Krause, E. 1971 *The Sociology of Occupations.* Boston: Little, Brown and Company.

Kronus, C.L. 1976 "The Evolution of Occupational Control: An Historical Study of Task Boundaries Between Physicians and Pharmacists." *Sociology of Work and Occupations,* 3:3–37.

Kropotkin, P. 1972 *Mutual Aid [1912].* London: Penguin.

Laderman, C. 1983 *Wives and Midwives: Childbirth and Nutrition in Rural Malaysia.* Berkeley: University of California Press.

Ladurie, Le Roy 1978 *Montaillou [1975].* London: Scolar Press.

Laforce, H. 1990 "The Different Stages of the Elimination of the Midwife in Quebec." In K. Arnup *et al.* (eds.), pp. 36–50. *Delivering Motherhood.* New York: Routledge.

Laget, M. 1980 "Childbirth in Seventeenth- and Eighteenth-Century France: Obstetrical Practices and Collective Attitudes." In R. Forster and O. Ranum (eds.), *Medicine and Society in France.* Baltimore: Johns Hopkins University Press.

Lamaze, F. 1955 *Painless Childbirth: The Lamaze Method.* New York: Pocket Books.

Langness, L. L. and G. Frank 1981 *Lives: An Anthropological Approach to Biography.* Novato, Calif.: Chandler & Sharp.

Larson, M. S. 1977 *The Rise of Professionalism: A Sociological Analysis.* Berkeley: University of California Press.

Lasch, C. 1978 *Haven in a Heartless World.* New York: Basic Books.

Lewis, J. 1980 *The Politics of Motherhood*. London: Croom Helm.

Leavitt, J. 1978 *Sickness and Health in America*. Madison: University of Wisconsin Press.

_____ 1986 *Brought to Bed: Birthing Women and Their Physicians in America, 1750*. New York: Oxford University Press.

Leveen, D. 1986 "Unionising Midwifery in California." In. P. Eakins (ed.), The American Way of Birth, pp. 292–328. Philadelphia: Temple University Press.

Light, D. 1986 "The Widening Gap Between Medical Training and Health Care Needs." *Sociologia Internationalis*, 1:43–52.

Lindesmith, A. 1968 *Addiction and Opiates*. Chicago: Aldine.

Litoff, J. 1978 *American Midwives*. Westport, Conn.: Greenview Press.

_____ 1986 *The American Midwife Debate*. New York: Greenwood Press.

Lofland, J. 1971 *Analyzing Social Settings*. Belmont: Wadsworth.

Lukes, S. 1973 *Emile Durkheim, His Life and Work: A Historical and Cultural Study*. London: Allen Lane.

Luxton, M. 1980 *More Than A Labour of Love*. Toronto: The Women's Press.

Macintyre, S. 1977 "The Management of Childbirth: A Review of Sociological Research Issues." *Social Science and Medicine*, 11:477–84.

Mandel, E. 1975 *Late Capitalism*. New Left Books.

Mannheim, K. 1936 *Ideology and Utopia [1929]*. London: Routledge & Kegan Paul.

Marsden, L. 1977 "Power Within a Profession: Medicine in Ontario." *Sociology of Work and Occupations*, 4:2–25.

Marshall, T. H. 1939 "The Recent History of Professionalism in Relation to Social Structure and Social Policy." *Canadian Journal of Economic and Political Science*, 5(3):325–40.

_____ 1963 *Sociology at the Crossroads*. London: Heinemann.

Marx, K. 1964 *The Economic and Philosophic Manuscripts of 1844* [first publ. 1932]. New York: International Publishers.

_____ 1977 *Selected Writings*, D. McLellan (ed). Oxford: University of Oxford Press.

_____ and F. Engels 1947 *The German Ideology [1844*; first publ. 1932]. New York: International Publishers.

Matthews, R. 1976 *There's No Better Place Than Here: Social Change in Three Newfoundland Communities*. Toronto: Peter Martin Associates.

Mauss, M. 1967 *The Gift [1925]*. New York: Norton.

McKinlay, J. 1982 "Toward the Proletarianisation of Physicians." In C. Derber, *Professionals at Work*, pp. 37–62. Boston: G. K. Hall.

McLaren, A. and A. McLaren 1986 *The Bedroom and the State*. Toronto: McClelland and Stewart.

Mead, M. 1935 *Sex and Temperament in Three Primitive Societies*. London: Routledge.

Mead, M. and N. Newton 1967 "Cultural Patterning of Perinatal Behaviour." In S. Richardson and A. Guttmacher (eds.), *Childbearing: Its Social and Psychological Aspects*. Baltimore: Williams and Wilkins.

Melosh, B. 1982 *"The Physician's Hand": Work Culture and Conflict in American Nursing*. Philadelphia: Temple University Press.

Merton, R. K. 1957 *Social Theory and Social Structure*, rev. and enl. ed.. New York: The Free Press.

_____ 1972 "Insiders and Outsiders: A Chapter in the Sociology of Knowledge." *American Journal of Sociology*, 78:9–47.

_____ 1975 "Structural Analysis in Sociology." In P. Blau (ed.), *Approaches to the Study of Social Structure*, pp. 21–52. New York: The Free Press.

_____ A.P. Gray, B. Hockey and H. C. Selvin (eds.) 1964 *Reader in Bureaucracy*. New York: The Free Press.

_____ R. Reader and P. L. Kendall 1957 *The Student-Physician*. Cambridge, Mass.: Harvard University Press.

Miller, L. 1962 "The Newfoundland Department of Health." St. John's, Nfld.: Department of Health.

Millerson, G. 1964 *The Qualifying Associations*. London: Routledge & Kegan Paul.

Mills, C. Wright 1951 *White Collar*. New York: Oxford University Press.

_____ 1959 *The Sociological Imagination*. New York: Oxford University Press.

Mishler, E. G. 1984 *The Discourse of Medicine: Dialectics of Medical Interviews*. Norwood, N. J.: Ablex Publishers.

Mongeau, B., H. L. Smith and A. C. Maney 1961 "The Granny Midwife: Changing Roles and Functions of a Folk Practitioner." *American Journal of Sociology*, 66:497–505.

Montagna, P. 1968 "Professionalisation and Bureaucratisation in Large Professional Organisations." *American Journal of Sociology*, 74:138–45.

Myrdal, A. and G. Myrdal 1945 *Crisis in Population Growth*. Stockholm: Bonniers.

Navarro, V. 1975 "Health and the Corporate Society." *Social Policy*, 5(5):41–49.

Neary, P. & J. Hiller (eds.) 1980 *Newfoundland in the Nineteenth and Twentieth Centuries*. Toronto: University of Toronto Press.

Nelson, M. 1986 "Birth and Social Class." In P. Eakins (ed.), *The American Way of Birth*, pp. 142–174. Philadelphia: Temple University Press.

Nevitt, J. 1978 *White Caps and Black Bands*. St. John's, Nfld.: Jesperson Press.

O'Brien, M. 1981 *The Politics of Reproduction*. London: Routledge & Kegan Paul.

Oakley, A. 1976 "Wisewoman and Medicine Man: Changes in the Management of Childbirth." In J. Mitchell and A. Oakley (eds.), *The Rights and Wrongs of Women*. Harmondsworth, Penguin.

Oakley, A. 1980 *Becoming a Mother*. New York: Schocken Books.

_____ 1984 *The Captured Womb*. Oxford, Basil Blackwell.

_____ and S. Houd 1986 "Alternative Perinatal Services: Report on a Pilot Survey." In J.M.L. Phaff, *Perinatal Health Services in Europe: Searching for Better Childbirth*, pp. 17–47. London: Croom Helm.

Oppenheimer, J. 1983 "Childbirth in Ontario: The Transition from Home to Hospital in the Early Twentieth Century." *Ontario History*, 65(1):36–60.

Oppenheimer, M. 1973 "The Proletarianisation of the Professional." *Sociological Review Monographs*, 20:213–27.

O'Reilly, W., P. Eakins, M. Gilfix & G. Richwald 1986 "Childbirth and the Malpractice Insurance Industry." In P. Eakins (ed.), *The American Way of Birth*, pp. 196–212. Philadelphia: Temple University Press.

O'Toole, R. and A. 1981 "Negotiating Interorganisational Orders." *Sociological Quarterly*, 22:29–41.

Park, R. E. 1928 "Human Migration and the Marginal Man." *American Journal of Sociology*, 33: 881–93.

_____ 1974 *Perspectives in Social Inquiry*. New York: Arno Press.

_____ and E. W. Burgess 1970 *Introduction to the Science of Sociology [1921]*. Chicago: The University of Chicago Press.

Parsons, T. 1951 *The Social System*. New York: The Free Press.

_____ 1954 "The Professions and Social Structure." *Essays in Sociological Theory*, pp. 34–49. Glencoe, Ill.

_____ 1968 "Professions." *International Encyclopedia of the Social Sciences*, 536–47. New York: Macmillan.

Pavolko, R. 1971 *Sociology of Occupations and Professions*. Itasca, Ill.: F.E. Peacock Publishers.

Perrucci, R. and J. E. Gerstl (eds.) 1969 *The Engineers and the Social System*. New York: John Wiley.

Peterson, M. J. 1978 *The Medical Profession in Mid-Victorian England*. Berkeley: University of California Press.

Pfeffer, J. and G. Salanick 1978 *The External Control of Organisations*. New York: Harper & Row.

Phaff, J.M.L. (ed.) 1975 *Midwives in Europe*. Strasbourg: Council of Europe.

_____ (ed.) 1986 *Perinatal Health Services in Europe: Searching for Better Childbirth*. London: Croom Helm.

Popper, K. 1959 *The Logic of Scientific Discovery*. New York: Harper & Row.

Potts M., B. Janowitz and J.A. Fortney (eds.) 1983 *Childbirth in Developing Countries*. Boston: MTP Press.

Poulantzas, N. 1975 *Classes in Contemporary Capitalism [1974]*. London: New Left Books.

Presthus, R. V. 1962 *The Organisational Society*. New York: Vintage Books.

Regan, T. 1984 "Some Limits to the Hospital as a Negotiated Order." *Social Science and Medicine*, 18:243-9.

_____ 1986 "Bargaining and Governmental Directives: The Question of Limits to Negotiated Orders." *The Canadian Review of Sociology and Anthropology*, 23(3):383-98.

Reinharz, S. 1979 *On Becoming A Social Scientist*. San Francisco: Jossey-Bass.

Report of the Royal Commission on Hospital and Nursing Home Costs 1984 St. John's, Nfld.: February 15, 1984.

Rich, A. 1975 "The Theft of Childbirth." *The New York Review of Books*, 22:25-30.

Ritzer, G. and D. Walczak 1988 "Rationalisation and the Deprofessionalisation of Physicians." *Social Forces*, 67(1):1-22.

Romalis, S. 1981 *Childbirth: Alternatives to Medical Control*. Austin: University of Texas Press.

Rooth, G. 1979 "Better Perinatal Health: Sweden." *Lancet II*, 8153:1170-72.

Rosenberg, C. (ed.) 1979 *Healing and History*. New York: Science History Publications.

Ross, G. 1978 "Marxism and the New Middle Class." *Theory and Society*, 5(2):163-90.

Ross, J. 1965 *The Role of the Cottage Hospital in Newfoundland Outport Medical Care*. St. John's, Nfld.: Department of Health.

Rossi, A. 1977 "A Biosocial Perspective on Parenting." *Daedalus*, 1–31.

Roth, J. 1963 *Timetables*. New York: Bobbs-Merrill.

_____ 1974 "Professionalism: The Sociologist's Decoy." *Sociology of Work and Occupations*, 1:6–23.

Rothman, B.K. 1982 *In Labour: Women and Power in the Birthplace*. New York: W.W. Norton Co.

_____ 1983 "Midwives in Transition." *Social Problems*, 30(3):262–71.

Rothman, R.A. 1984 "Deprofessionalisation: The Case of Law in America." *Work and Occupations*, 2(2):183–206.

Rueschemeyer, D. 1986 *Power and the Division of Labour*. Cambridge: Polity Press.

Ruzek, S. 1978 *The Women's Health Movement: Feminist Alternatives to Medical Control*. New York: Praeger Publishers.

Sahlins, M. 1965 "On the Sociology of Primitive Exchange." In M. Banton (ed.), *The Relevance of Models of Social Anthropology*. London: Tavistock.

Salaff, J. 1981 *Working Daughters of Hong Kong*. Cambridge: Cambridge University Press.

Schrader, C. 1987 *Mother and Child were Saved*. Amsterdam: Rodopi.

Scholten, C. 1985 *Childbearing in American Society*. New York: New York University Press.

Scott, W.R. 1966 "Professionals in Bureaucracies—Areas of Conflict." In H. M. Vollmer and D. L. Mills (eds.), *Professionalisation*, pp. 265–75. Englewood Cliffs, N. J.: Prentice-Hall.

_____ 1969 "Professional Employees in a Bureaucratic Structure: Social Work." In A. Etzioni (ed.), *The Semi-Professions and Their Organisation*, pp. 82.140. New York: Free Press.

_____ 1981 *Organisations, Rational, Natural and Open Systems*. Englewood Cliffs.N. J.: Prentice-Hall.

Scully, D. 1980 *Men Who Control Women's Health*. Boston: Houghton Mifflin.

Segal, L. 1987 *Is the Future Female: Troubled Thoughts on Contemporary Feminism*. London: Virago Press.

Seward, R. Seward, J. and V. Natoli 1984 "Different Approaches to Childbirth and Their Consequences in Italy, Sweden, and the United States." *International Journal of Sociology of the Family*, 14:1–16.

Shaw, N.S. 1974 *Forced Labor: Maternity Care in the United States*. New York: Pergamon Press.

Shorter, E. 1982 *A History of Women's Bodies*. New York: Basic Books.

Sigerist.H. 1936 "An Outline of the Development of the Hospital." *Bulletin of the History of Medicine*, 4:573–81.

Simmel, G. 1971 *On Individual and Social Forms*, [1908], ed. D. Levine. Chicago: The University of Chicago Press.

Simpson, I. H. 1979 *From Student to Nurse*. Cambridge: Cambridge University Press.

Smigel, E. 1964 *The Wall Street Lawyer*. Bloomington: Indiana University Press.

Smith, D. 1980 "A Sociology for Women." In J. Sherman and J Beck (eds.), *The Prism of Sex*, pp. 135–87. Madison: University of Wisconsin Press.

Smith, H. L. 1958 "Contingencies of Professional Differentiation." *American Journal of Sociology*, 63:410–14.

Sorensen, J. and J. Sorensen 1974 "The Conflict of Professionals in Bureaucratic Organisations," *Administrative Science Quarterly*, 19:98–106.

Sorokin, P. 1927 *Social Mobility*. New York: Harper & Row.

Spencer, H. 1896 *Principles of Sociology*, Vol. 3. New York: Appleton.

Starr, P. *The Social Transformation of American Medicine*. New York: Basic Books.1982.

Stevens, R. 1971 *American Medicine and the Public Interest*. New Haven: Yale University Press.

Stinchombe, A. L. 1972 "Social Structure and Organisations." In M. Brinkerhoff and P. Kunz (eds.), *Complex Organisations and Their Environments*, pp. 123–40. Dubuque, Iowa: WM. C. Brown Co.

Story, G.M., W.J. Kirwin and J.A. Widdowson 1982 *Dictionary of Newfoundland English*. Toronto: University of Toronto Press.

Strauss, A. 1978 *Negotiations: Varieties, Processes, and Social Order*. San Francisco: Jossey-Bass Publishers.

Sudnow, D. 1967 *Passing On: The Social Organisation of Dying*. Englewood Cliffs, N. J.: Prentice-Hall.

Sussman, G. 1982 *Selling Mother's Milk: The Wet-Nursing Business in France 1715–1914*. Urbana: University of Illinois Press.

Tawney, R. H. 1937 *The Acquisitive Society [1921]*. London: G. Bell.

Teijlingen, E. & P. McCaffery 1987 "The Profession of Midwife in the Netherlands." *Midwifery*, 3:178–86.

Thomas, W. I. and F. Znaniecki 1927 *The Polish Peasant in Europe and America*. New York: Knopf.

Tomasson, R. 1970 *Sweden: Prototype of Modern Society*. New York: Random House.

Thompson, E. P. 1966 *The Making of the English Working Class*. New York: Vintage Books.

Thompson, J. D. and W. J. McEwen 1972 "Organisational Goals and Environment: Goal Setting as an Interaction Process." In M. Brinkerhoff and P. Kunz (eds)., *Complex Organisations and Their Environments*, pp. 255–67. Dubuque, Iowa: WM. C. Brown Co.

Thompson, V. 1964 *Modern Organisation*. New York: Basic Books.

Toren, N. 1975 "Deprofessionalisation and Its Sources: A Preliminary Analysis." *Sociology of Work and Occupations*, 2(4):323–38.

Touraine, A. 1974 *The Academic System in American Society*. New York: McGraw-Hill.

_____ 1981 "The New Social Conflicts: Crisis or Transformation." In C. Lemert (ed.), *French Sociology: Rupture and Renewal Since 1968*, pp. 313–41. New York: Columbia University Press.

Veblen, T. 1921 *The Engineers and the Price System*. New York: The Viking Press.

Vogel, M. 1980 *The Invention of the Modern Hospital*. Chicago: The University of Chicago Press.

Vollmer, H. M. and D. L. Mills 1966 *Professionalisation*. Englewood Cliffs, N. J.: Prentice-Hall.

Wagner, D. 1980 "The Proletarianisation of Nursing in the United States, 1932–46." *International Journal of Health Services*, 10(2):271–90.

Waitzkin, H. and B. Waterman 1974 *The Exploitation of Illness in Capitalist Society*. New York: Bobbs-Merrill.

Walker, J. 1972 "The Changing Role of the Midwife." *International Journal of Nursing Studies*, 9:85–94.

Walsh, D. 1989 "Comparison of Management and Outcome of Labour under Two Systems of Care." *Midwives Chronicle*, 102:270–73.

Warburton, R. and W. Carroll 1988 "Class and Gender in Nursing." In B. Bolaria and H. Dickinson (eds.), *Sociology of Health in Canada*, pp. 365–74. Toronto: Harcourt Brace Jovanovich.

Warren, C. 1988 *Gender Issues in Field Research*. Beverly Hills: Sage Publications.

Wax, R. 1971 *Doing Fieldwork*. Chicago: The University of Chicago Press.

Weber, M. 1958 *The Protestant Ethic and the Spirit of Capitalism [1905–5]*, trans. T. Parsons. New York: Charles Scribner's Sons.

_____ 1978 *Economy and Society [1922]*, Vols. I & II, ed. G. Roth and C. Wittich. Berkeley, Calif.: University of California Press.

Weick, K.E. 1976 "Educational Organizations as Loosely Coupled Systems." *Administrative Science Quarterly*, 21:1–19.

Weisner, M.E. 1983 "Early Modern Midwifery: A Case Study." *International Journal of Women's Studies*, 16(1):26–43.

Weitz, R. and D. Sullivan 1985 "Licensed Lay Midwifery and the Medical Model of Childbirth." *Sociology of Health and Illness*, 7(1):36–54.

Wertz, R.W. and D.C. Wertz 1977 *Lying-In: A History of Childbirth in America*. New York: Schocken Books.

Whyte, W. F. 1948 *Human Relations in the Restaurant Industry*. New York: McGraw-Hill.

Whyte, W. H. 1957 *The Organisation Man*. New York: Doubleday Anchor Books.

Wilensky, H. 1964 "The Professionalisation of Everyone?" *American Journal of Sociology*, 69:137–58.

Williams, R. 1973 *The Country and the City*. New York: Oxford University Press.

Willis, E. 1983 *Medical Dominance: The Division of Labour in Australian Health Care*. London: George Allen & Unwin.

Wolf, M. 1985 *Revolution Postponed: Women in Contemporary China*. California.: Standard University Press.

WHO 1981 *World Health Statistics*. Geneva.

Wright, E. O. 1980 "Class, Occupation, and Organisation." *International Yearbook of Organisation Studies*. London: Routledge & Kegan Paul.

Wrigley, E.A. 1969 *Population and History*. New York: McGraw-Hill.

Zola, I. 1972 "Medicine as an Institution of Social Control." *Sociological Review*, 20:487–504.

_____ 1975 "In the Name of Health and Illness: On Some Socio-political Consequences of Medical Influence." *Social Science and Medicine*, 9.

_____ 1983 *Socio-Medical Inquiries: Recollections, Reflections, and Reconsiderations*. Philadelphia: Temple University Press.

Index

ISER BOOKS

Papers

Mailing Address:
ISER Books (Institute of Social and Economic Research)
Memorial University of Newfoundland
St. John's, Newfoundland, Canada, A1C 5S7